Sugar and Spice

a collection of recipes for
and by my friends
by

Sally Goldman

original illustrations
by

Pat Wozniak

PEPPERMILL PRESS, INC.

Honolulu, Hawaii

This book is dedicated to my
husband, Monte Goldman, a most gracious
host—and my four daughters,
Amie, Beth, Meghan, and Leslie,
because they like my cooking.

Sugar and Spice is a collection of recipes from my friends
who enjoy cooking and entertaining. Most of the recipes are
original. All the recipes have been successful for my friends
at their own parties. I thank each of them for their
enthusiasm and their contributions. Friends truly are the
Sugar and Spice of one's life.

Sally E. Goldman

Recipe for Friendship

Take:

1 well-rounded tablespoon of understanding
1 heaping teaspoon of support
3 good measures of honesty
1 overflowing cup of sharing

Combine all ingredients over a period of time,
being sure to add a generous sprinkling
of laughter. Serve generous portions and
savor well.

—anonymous

Contents

A Note on Entertaining

The success of a party, whether it is large or small, depends on the attitude and pre-planning of the host and/or hostess. If the hostess is relaxed and enjoying herself, her guests will also be relaxed and ready to have a good time. How does a hostess become relaxed? First, by having the party schedule planned and prepared, and second, by being enthusiastic about her party. Both of these points are equally important. No matter how small your party may be, make it have a purpose. For example, to introduce new friends, to celebrate a friend's birthday, or to try a new recipe or menu. When the hostess has a "purpose of party" in mind, she will be more comfortable, and ready to be the director of her party.

It is the duty of the hostess to be the director of her party. For example, she should be aware of shy guests and bring them into conversations. She should see that the food is served at the proper time. Do not serve food too soon after your guests arrive. Let them become comfortable in your home...and please do not serve dinner too late. One hour after guests arrive is perfect timing, if you have served appetizers during the cocktail hour.

Entertaining is as successful in a small apartment as it can be in a large home with servants. The graciousness of the host or hostess and the planning of the party will give it the spirit that counts. Your guests will feel honored and special.

My friends have supplied fun and delicious recipes for you to try. These are recipes that they have entertained with successfully. So, go ahead...plan a party!

Aloha,
Sally

rosemary

rosemary

Mediterranean origin...its Roman name, "rosemarinus," because it grows near the sea, can be poetically translated as "dew of the sea"...both its foliage and flowers are aromatic with a spicy, piny fragrance... it is an emblem of friendship and also stands for remembrance...the wood from its branches made excellent lutes in Renaissance times.

Menus

Special thanks to Wolf Lehmkuhl of the
Hyatt Regency Waikiki for his expert wine selections

Cocktails Only

Steak Tartar or Armenian Steak Tartar
Oysters Rockefeller   Diane's Japanese Chicken
Daffodil Dip   Extra Special Clam Dip
Snickerdoodles
Chardonnay or Coteaux Champagne

Picnics

Rhubarb Daiquiri
Tabasco Chicken   Perfect Potato Salad
Texas Baked Beans
Corn on the Cob   Spoon Bread
Chocolate Cake   Homemade Ice Cream
Macadamia Nut Shortbread
Rosé from Anjou or Sweet Rosé from California

Ladies Gourmet Picnic

Tabbouleh   Quiche
Fresh Strawberries with Sour Cream and Brown Sugar
Almond Squares   Lace Cookies
Fumé Blanc from California or Pouilly-Fumé

Gourmet Picnic

Scotch Eggs or Open-Faced Glazed Sandwiches
Chicken Wings
Poached Salmon in Aspic   Dill Mayonnaise
Artichoke Rice Salad
or
Pea Salad
Devil's Food Cake and Miniature Pecan Tarts
Sauvignon Blanc

The Junior Set

Stacy's Pasta Salad
Amie's "My Chicken"
Best Chocolate Cake in the World
or
Pineapple Lime Jello Salad
Carson's Shrimp
Butter Pecan Elegance Cake
Guava Nectar

Italian Lunch

Tomato Mozzarella Salad
Cannelloni Ranieri
Iced Zabaglione
Soavé Classico

Gourmet Dinners

Paté Maison
Coquilles St. Jacques – Gewürztztraminer (Alsace)
Individual Beef Wellingtons   Chardonnay
Wild Rice   Fresh Baby Carrots
Salad Vintner   Nuit St. Georges
Hot Raspberry Souffle

Boursin Cheese
Cold Cucumber Soup
Pork Paprika with Spaetzle
German Brussel Sprouts
Apple Crêpes with Calvados
Egri – Bikaver or Austrian Red Wine

Italian Dinner

Antipasto   Turino Toast
Italian Chicken   Linguine à la Filomena
Bibb Lettuce with Vinaigrette Dressing
Pasticcini di Napoli
Orvietto   Bandolino

Natural Gourmet Dinner

Jerry's California Seafood Bisque
Spinach Salad   Eggplant Parmesan
Baked Cheesecake
California Chardonnay

Barbecue Dinner

Salmon Mousse   Marinated Mushrooms
Caesar Salad
Butterflied Lamb with Mango Chutney
Texas Monterey Cheese Rice
Velvet Hammer   Chocolate Mint Sticks
Gewürztraminer

Wild Game Dinner

Caviar Log
Wild Duck
Riverside Casserole
Wild Rice   Spinach Salad   Rolls
Peaches Flambé or Frozen Lemon Pie

Ladies Elegant Luncheon

Escargot Soup
Cold Lobster
Lemon Pie
Chablis

Gentlemen's Lunch

Cold Caviar Consomme
Chicken Dijon   Spinach Mold
Gourmet Rice
Kentucky Derby Pie
Mersault or other Burgundy

Lunches

Mamosa
Cold Cucumber Watercress Soup
Fabulous Chicken Salad in Papaya
Meringue Surprises
Johannesburg Riesling from California
or
Light Moselle Riesling

Cantaloupe Soup
Oriental Chicken Salad
Lemon Walnut Muffins
Frozen Delight
Light Rheingau

Sangria Blanca
Chili Con Queso
Best Ever No Bean Dip with Chips
Taco Salad   Chili Rellenos
Rum Cake

Ladies Brunch

Champagne Punch or good California Sparkling Wine
Cheese Souffle Roll
Curried Fruit
Orange Muffins and Bran Muffins

Sunday Morning Football Brunch

Bloody Marys
Brunch Casserole   Baked Papaya
Chicken Livers with Cumin
Applesauce Loaf   Sour Cream Muffins
Brownies
Imported Pitcher Beer

Coffee

Coffee Punch

Artichoke Squares   Lychee Stuffed with Cream Cheese

Hot Sausage Pick-Ups

Jewish Coffee Cake   Poi Muffins

California Johannesburg Riesling

Casual Winter Buffet Dinner

Samosa and Vegetable Dip

Shrimp Curry with Mango Chutney

Rice

Ada's Rolls

Pudding Cake or Marilyn's Chocolate Dessert

Mulled Cider or Rhine Wine

One Dish Dinner

Cassola de Peix

Mixed Green Salad   Ginger Dressing

Chocolate Cake with Orange Liqueur

Dry Red Wine

Late Supper after Theater

Champagne Brut

Broiled Grapefruit

Eggs Alexander

Kahlua Mousse

Coffee Jerome

Holiday Dinner

Blender Borsht
Overnight Turkey with Stuffing
Mashed Potatoes and Giblet Gravy
Sweet Potato Balls
or
Sweet Potatoes with Apricots
Green Bean Casserole
Molded Cranberry Salad　　　Easy Refrigerator Rolls
Pumpkin Pie　　　Wonderful Walnut Pie
California Zinfandel

Soup Buffet in Aspen

Spinach Puffs with Mustard Sauce
Chipped Beef Balls
Turkey Soup with Quenelles
Split Pea Soup　　　Cioppino
or
Mushroom Soup　　　Crab Bisque
Onion Corn Bread　　　Mondel Bread
Texas Praline Cheese Cake
or
Cream Cheese Dessert
Red and White Dry Wine

Polynesian Dinner

Lomi Salmon　　　Art's Poki
Tahitian Raw Fish
New Zealand Salad
Lau-Lau　　　Hawaiian Chicken
Papaya Poi
Mele's Hawaiian Wedding Cakes
Tropical Drinks or California Johannisberg Riesling

mint

mint

Mediterranean origin…once it was believed that the odor of mint sharpened the perceptions, so Pliny of Rome recommended that his students wear wreaths of mint while studying…sailors used it to purify their drinking water, and today, the Arabs favor mint tea as a social drink, while in North Africa and Persia, cuisines rely on mint as an addition to many foods.

Beverages

champagne punch

2 bottles champagne (fifths)
2 bottles sauterne (fifths)
1 quart soda water
1/2 cup brandy
1/2 cup Grand Marnier
1/2 cup honey

Chill all the ingredients so they are ice cold. Chill the punch bowl if possible. When you are ready to serve the punch, remove the fruit from the freezer.* Fill the punch bowl with the chilled ingredients and place the frozen fruit in the center. Makes 5 quarts or about 40 4-oz. servings.

*…frozen fruit such as strawberries, cherries, grapes, plums, may be used instead of ice cubes so the punch is not diluted.

Lavonne Tollerud – Honolulu, Hawaii

sangria blanca

1/2 gallon dry white wine (jug)
1 cup apple juice
4 tablespoons sugar
1 lime, sliced
1 lemon, sliced
1 orange, sliced
3 ounces Grand Marnier or Triple Sec

Combine all ingredients, except Grand Marnier, and let stand overnight. Add liqueur just before serving in a glass punch bowl.

Sugar and Spice

margaritas

6 ounces tequila
3 ounces Triple Sec
1 tablespoon egg white
6 ounces mix (recipe follows)

mix

1 can daiquiri mix
1 can frozen lemonade
10 ounces sweet and sour bar mix

Combine all ingredients in a blender and mix well.

Marjorie Wilson – Honolulu, Hawaii

rhubarb daiquiri

3 teaspoons rhubarb sauce*
2 teaspons powdered lemonade
2 ounces rum

Put sauce in blender or food processor for a short time so it isn't stringy.

Mix all ingredients with crushed ice or enough water to fill an 8 ounce glass. Serves 1.

*see sauces

Betty and Art Pfister – Aspen, Colorado

frozen daiquiri

1 can lemonade (frozen)
1 can water
2 cans light rum
1 small bottle 7-up

Combine all ingredients and then put in freezer. Stir before serving.

Jessie Brown – Honolulu, Hawaii

eggnog

2 dozen eggs
2-1/4 cups sugar
2 quarts whipping cream
2 fifths bourbon
1 fifth rum

Separate egg yolks from whites the night before. Beat yolks well, add sugar, bourbon and rum. Let stand overnight. A few hours before serving, beat egg whites and cream. Fold cream and beaten egg whites into egg yolk mixture. Do not stir in, just fold. Keep chilled until ready to serve. Top with ground nutmeg. Serves 30.

Sugar and Spice

julglogg

2 bottles dry red wine
4 whole cloves
1 2-inch piece cinnamon stick
slivers of orange peel from 2 oranges
1/2 cup almonds, blanched and slivered
1/2 cup raisins
sugar to taste

In a three-quart sauce pan combine all but the sugar and simmer for 1 hour. Stir sugar (1/2 cup if you don't want it too sweet) into hot wine and stir until dissolved. Heat but do not boil. Serve glogg hot. In Scandinavia they sometimes add a bottle of aquavit and ignite. Pour into heat-proof glass cups and garnish with a cinnamon stick in each.

If you have a glass pot with a light under it, this is both delicious and attractive to serve for a change from the bar (or your stove) in winter. Serves 12-15.

Linda Janovic – New York, New York

hot cider toddy

Warm apple cider or just apple juice with a cinnamon stick, sprinkle of cinnamon and allspice, a squeeze of lemon and/or orange and a thin slice of lemon. Get very hot and pour over desired amount of brandy. (About 3-4 parts cider to 1 part brandy). Stir and garnish with cinnamon stick.

Linda Janovic – New York, New York

spiced tea

3 quarts boiling water
1-3/4 cups sugar
juice and rind from 1 lemon
2 oranges
2 teaspoons whole cloves
4 sticks cinnamon
1-1/2 tablespoons tea

Combine first 6 ingredients and let stand for 20 minutes, keeping hot. Add tea, and let stand 5 minutes. Strain, serve hot.

Terease Hampton – Ponca City, Oklahoma

coffee punch

1-1/2 cups instant coffee
3 cups boiling water
1-1/2 cups sugar
1 teaspoon salt
3 tablespoons vanilla
1-1/4 gallons milk
3 gallons vanilla ice cream

Mix coffee in hot water, add sugar, salt, vanilla and milk. Chill. Immediately before serving, add ice cream which has been softened, just enough to break up in the coffee mixture. It is best added in small amounts as it is served. Serves 40 to 45.

Nancy Kennedy – Honolulu, Hawaii

the coffee jerome

1-1/2 ounces Amaretto di Saronna
8 ounces strong black coffee
freshly whipped cream, flavored with
    sugar and vanilla to taste

Combine liqueur and coffee in a pre-heated, tulip-shaped glass, fill to 1/2 inch of rim. Float whipped cream generously on top.

...this classically simple drink was introduced on December 23, 1972 by J. Michael Solheim at his Hotel Jerome Bar in Aspen, Colorado.

...on that cold winter's day, in the late afternoon, a dampened group of skiers first experienced the coffee Jerome. As all skiers know, those first moments after coming off the slopes, and inside to the fire, the warmth and sounds of après ski are a super-charged experience.

...that noisy afternoon in the Jerome bar, a tray of coffee Jerome was set before these skiers. As each person sipped the warm amber combination, an expression of surprise and satisfaction occurred. This mutual appreciation is seen whenever the coffee Jerome is served.

...there have been many attempted imitations of this fine drink but none can ever equal the experience of those skiers back in 1972 of that which is now awaiting you and your friends. Enjoy!

J. Michael Solheim – Aspen, Colorado

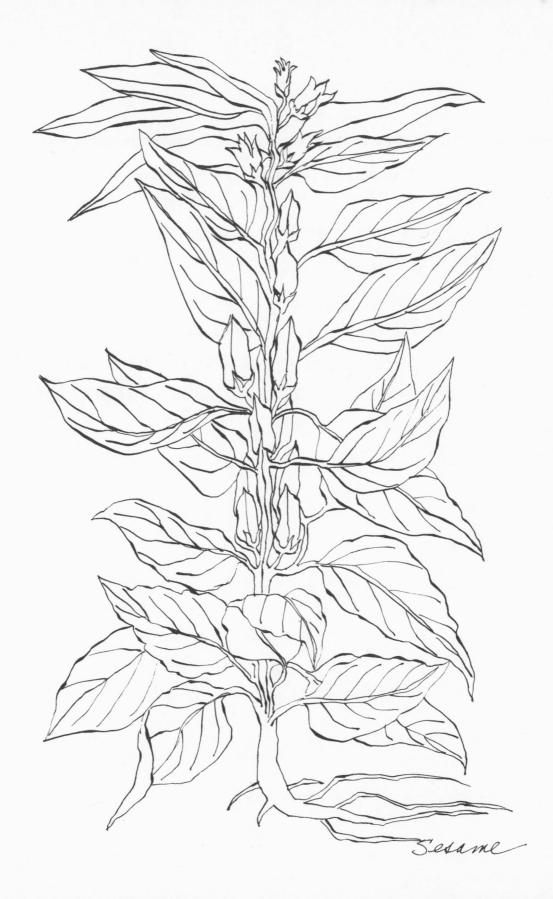

Sesame

sesame

Asian origin...one of man's oldest foods,
both seeds and oil were important ingredients...well known confections from
middle eastern "halvah" and "pita"
bread have these seeds as important ingredients, and one of the food staples of the
same part of the world is a sauce called
"tehina" in which the seed is ground into
a mayonnaise-like consistency and seasoned.

Appetizers

antipasto

sauce

1 cup each: catsup, chili sauce and water
1/2 cup each: olive oil, tarragon vinegar
    and lemon juice
1 clove garlic, minced
2 tablespoons brown sugar
1 tablespoon each: Worcestershire sauce
    and prepared mustard
salt to taste
dash of cayenne

salad

1/2 head cauliflower
3 medium carrots
2 stalks celery
1/2 pound small whole mushrooms
1 8-ounce jar small peppers
    (peperoncini) – drained
1 12.5-ounce can tuna
1 cup tiny onions – frozen, thawed
1 can cut green beans, drained
1 jar marinated artichoke hearts

garnish: black olives, green olives, parsley

Put the sauce ingredients in a large pan. Bring to a boil and simmer for a few minutes. Cut the cauliflower into flowerettes, and the carrots and celery into 1/2-inch pieces. Drain the artichokes and cut in halves. Add the first 5 vegetable ingredients and simmer slowly for 20 minutes. Add the tuna, onions, green beans and artichokes and simmer a few minutes longer. Cool, then chill. Serve in individual bowls or from one large bowl garnished with the sliced olives and parsley.

Marjane Wall – San Francisco, California

cheese delice from switzerland

1/2 pound butter
3-3/4 cups flour
1-1/2 quarts milk
1 pound emmanthaller cheese
1 pound gruyere cheese
12 egg yolks
salt and pepper
egg wash (slightly beaten egg)
fine dry bread crumbs
olive oil

Melt butter and blend in flour, cook and stir until golden. Add milk and cook over low heat until thick and smooth. Remove from heat, blend in grated cheese. Add egg yolks, mix well…season with salt and pepper. Turn into a pyrex glass meat loaf pan and chill or freeze overnight. If frozen, thaw and cut into 1/2-inch slices, shape into croquettes and dip in egg wash. Roll in crumbs, and saute in hot olive oil. Sprinkle with parsley. Serve immediately with a nice chilled fruity white wine. Garnish with parsley.

You can make this up in two or four batches from the recipe and freeze almost indefinitely. When you are ready to use thaw to a point that you can get a knife through the cheese. Do not thaw too much or it will be hard to handle. This recipe can be divided in half.

Lynda Brennan – Honolulu, Hawaii

cheese twist sticks

1 cup flour
1/2 teaspoon salt
1/2 teaspoon dry mustard
1/8 teaspoon cayenne
1/3 cup butter
1 cup grated cheddar
3 tablespoons ice water

Sift all dry ingredients. Cut in cheese and butter, add ice water and roll to a thickness of 1/8-inch. Cut in strips and twist. Bake at 350° for about 15 minutes.

Nancy Krueger – San Antonio, Texas

artichoke cheese squares

2 6-ounce jars marinated artichokes
2 tablespoons minced onion
1/8 teaspoon garlic salt
4 eggs
1/4 cup fine bread crumbs
1/4 teaspoon salt
1/2 pound sharp cheddar, grated
1/8 teaspoon pepper
1/8 teaspoon oregano
1/8 teaspoon Tabasco
2 tablespoons parsley

Drain marinade from jar into frying pan. Saute onion and garlic. Drain other jar and discard juice. Chop artichoke hearts. Beat egg and bread crumbs and seasonings. Stir in cheese, parsley, artichokes and onion mixture. Pour into a greased 9 x 11-inch pan. Bake at 325° for 30 minutes. Cool and cut into squares. Serve hot or cold. Makes 3 dozen.

Pi Beta Phi – Punches and Munches

gougere

1 cup water
1/2 cup (1 stick) butter
1 cup all purpose flour
4 eggs
1-1/2 cups grated gruyere cheese

1 teaspoon Dijon mustard
1 teaspoon salt
1/2 teaspoon dry mustard
dash of hot pepper sauce

Preheat oven to 450°. Lightly butter baking sheet. Combine water and butter in medium sauce pan, and bring to a rolling boil over medium heat. Make sure butter is completely melted. Add flour all at once and beat with a wooden spoon until mixture forms a ball and comes away from the sides of the pan. Remove from heat. Add eggs one at a time, beating vigorously after each addition, until dough is smooth and shiny. Blend in remaining ingredients.

On a baking sheet form a circle 9 inches in diameter by arranging tablespoonfuls of dough with sides touching. Repeat, making second layer of dough directly atop first. Bake 10 minutes. Reduce oven temperature to 325° and bake until gougere is puffed and lightly browned, about 15 minutes more. Immediately poke holes all around gougere with fork to let steam out. Slide onto serving plate and cut into wedges.

Mary Lou Brogan – Honolulu, Hawaii

crusty havarti appetizer

1 7-ounce round creamy havarti cheese
1 tablespoon Dijon mustard
1/4 cup chopped mixed fresh herbs such
    as basil, dill, sage, chives, parsley,
    thyme, etc…
3 frozen patty shells or 1/2 sheet frozen
    puff pastry, thawed
1 egg, lightly beaten
parsley for garnish

Spread top of cheese with mustard, then cover with mixed herbs, pressing them into the mustard. If using patty shells, arrange them close together in a triangle. Moisten edges that touch, and pinch them together.

Gently roll the dough into a 9-inch circle. Put the cheese in the center of the dough, herb-side down. Gather the edges of the pastry over the cheese, moistening the overlapping edges and pinching them together tightly. Place the package on a greased piece of aluminum foil, on a baking sheet, seam-side down. Brush with beaten egg, and chill for 30 minutes. Brush again with egg, and cup the foil closely around the sides of bundle and bake at 375° for 15 minutes. Brush again with egg and bake 15 minutes longer, or until golden brown. Let cool 20 to 30 minutes before cutting into wedges.

Shirley Dana – San Francisco, California

turino toast

6 slices stale french bread
2 eggs, beaten
1 cup Italian dry white wine
3/4 cup freshly grated Parmesan cheese
3 tablespoons butter

Trim crusts off the bread. Mix beaten eggs with cheese. Dip the bread slices in wine, one at a time, then dip the slices in the cheese and egg mixture coating them well. Arrange on a well buttered cookie sheet and dot with butter. Bake in a 375° oven for 15 minutes or until browned, turning the slices once. Serve hot. Serves 6.

You may serve this with salad or pasta or may use it as an appetizer.

Lynda Brennan – Honolulu, Hawaii

marietta cheese circle

1 pound sharp cheddar cheese, grated
1 cup macadamia nuts or pecans, finely
    chopped
3/4 cup mayonnaise
1 small onion, grated
dash of cayenne pepper

Mix well, using hands. Spray round mold generously with Pam. Press into
mold and chill. When ready to serve, remove from mold onto serving plate and
fill center of ring with strawberry preserves. Use with wheat crackers. Place 3 or 4
small knives close by for spreading. This is delicious. One ring serves 25 to 30.

Sugar and Spice

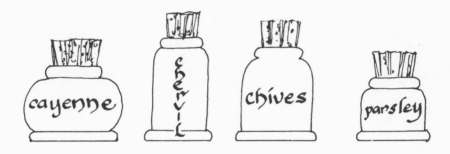

boursin cheese

1/2 teaspoon dried chervil
1 teaspoon dried chives
1/8 teaspoon salt
2 teaspoons dried parsley
1/2 teaspoon garlic powder
8 ounces cream cheese, softened

Pound herbs to a fine powder and mix with cream cheese. Serve with stone
ground wheat wafers.

…exactly like the French herbed cheese in the deli case.

Ruth Stebbins – Honolulu, Hawaii

duke's party dip

1 5-ounce bottle Pickapeppa Sauce
12 ounces cream cheese

Pour Pickapeppa over cream cheese. Serve with corn chips or wheat thins as a dip.

…Pickapeppa Sauce can be found in the gourmet section of the supermarket. Its spicy flavor is excellent with cocktails.

Duke Edwards – Ponca City, Oklahoma

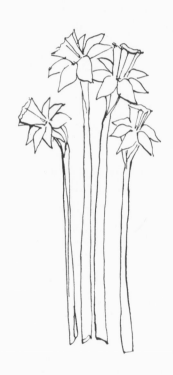

daffodil dip

1 8-ounce package cream cheese
1/2 cup mayonnaise
1 hard cooked egg
2 tablespoons onion
1 clove garlic
1/4 to 1/2 cup parsley
1 to 2 tablespoons anchovy paste

Cream together, cheese, mayonnaise, chopped egg white (reserve the yolk for garnish), minced onion, minced garlic, chopped parsley and anchovy paste. Top dip with crumbled egg yolk. Serve with fresh vegetable crudities.

…anchovy paste can be found in the gourmet section at the supermarket.

Judie Miura – Honolulu, Hawaii

broccoli guacamole

1 cup broccoli
2 tablespoons Parmesan cheese
1/4 cup cheddar cheese
1 teaspoon minced green onion
1/4 cup sour cream
1/4 cup mayonnaise
1/4 to 1/2 teaspoon curry powder
1/4 teaspoon salt
squeeze of lemon juice

Cook and chop broccoli. Grate cheese and mince onion. Puree all ingredients in a blender. Chill. Serve with corn chips and assorted vegetables. Serves 6.

Ruth Stebbins – Honolulu, Hawaii

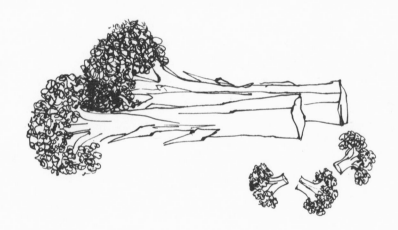

vegetable dip

1 cup sour cream
1 cup mayonnaise
1 tablespoon dill weed
1 tablespoon "beau monde" spice
1 tablespoon green onion, chopped
1 tablespoon fresh parsley

Mix ingredients together and serve with vegetables…a quick pupu and great for warm evenings.

Janee Dimmitt – Honolulu, Hawaii

glazed open faced sandwiches

1-2/3 cups strong chicken broth
1/4 teaspoon white pepper
1 bay leaf
1/2 teaspoon dill weed
1 package plain gelatin
1/2 teaspoon salt
4 tablespoons lemon juice
dash of cayenne pepper
6 slices rye or whole wheat bread

Combine the broth and all the seasonings and simmer for 10 minutes. Strain.
Dissolve the gelatin in 1/4 cup cold water. Add to the hot mixture and stir
until well melted. Chill until syrupy, either in a bowl of ice or in the refrigerator.
Arrange any combination of meats, vegetables, dressings or cheeses on your
bread slices. Place the bread slices on a metal rack set on a cookie sheet.
Carefully pour a thin layer of the gelatin mixture over the sandwiches. Chill
until just set but not firm. Then pour a second layer over each. Chill until firm,
about 1 hour. Decorate with parsley or watercress.

…you may slice each piece of bread in half before assembling, to serve more.

Lavonne Tollerud – Honolulu, Hawaii

marinated mushrooms

8 boxes mushrooms
2/3 cups salad oil
2 cups or less vinegar
4 teaspoons salt
4 cloves garlic, minced
4 teaspoons pepper
4 teaspoons sugar
4 tablespoons fresh parsley, or
    dried parsley

Clean mushrooms and cut off tips of stems. Set aside. Blend all other ingredients
and pour over mushrooms. Marinate in glass jars and refrigerate. Drain
before serving.

This is better prepared the day before.

Janee Dimmitt – Honolulu, Hawaii

boursin stuffed mushrooms

1/2 onion, diced fine
1/2 cup butter, divided
20 large mushrooms
1/2 container boursin cheese with garlic and herbs

Saute onion in 1/4 cup butter. Wash mushrooms. Remove and chop stems in pieces. Place caps in baking pan. Add stem pieces to onion and cook briefly. Remove from heat and add boursin cheese, mixing just until combined. Melt remaining 1/4 cup butter and brush over mushroom caps. Fill each with mixture and broil 8 to 10 minutes. Serve at once.

Shannon Lowrey – Honolulu, Hawaii

super-duper yummy mushroom rollups

dough

1 cup flour
1/2 teaspoon salt
1/2 cup butter
1/4 pound cottage cheese
3 tablespoons sesame or caraway seeds

filling

1 pound mushrooms
2 tablespoons butter
salt and pepper to taste

onion salt to taste
melted butter
1 egg, beaten

To make dough, place flour in a bowl, with salt. Cut in butter until it is the size of small peas. Stir in cottage cheese and press together into a ball. Refrigerate overnight or at least 2 hours.

To make filling, coarsely chop mushrooms and saute them in butter. Season with salt, pepper and onion salt, and set aside. Sprinkle floured pastry cloth with the sesame seeds. Roll dough into a rectangle, about 15 x 8 inches, cut in half lengthwise. Spread with melted butter. Put half of the mushroom filling lengthwise along the edge. Roll up as for a jelly roll. Place roll on baking sheet. Repeat for remaining strip. Refrigerate for about 1 hour. When ready to bake, brush with beaten egg and sprinkle with onion salt. Cut into 1 inch pieces. Bake at 400° for 15 minutes.

These are not easy to roll or transfer. Just do your best!

Linda Janovic – New York, New York

paté maison

1 cup butter
1 pound chicken livers
1 medium onion
1/2 teaspoon paprika
1/8 teaspoon salt
1/8 teaspoon fresh ground pepper
1 tablespoon cognac
3/4 cup pimento stuffed olives, sliced

Melt 1/4 cup butter in a saucepan. Add chicken livers, onions, paprika, salt and pepper. Cover and cook over low heat for 8 minutes. Blend mixture in an electric blender until smooth. Add cognac and remaining butter and blend in. Chill until firm. Mold the mixture into shape of 1/2 pineapple and cover with sliced olives. Serve with crackers. Makes 2-1/2 cups.

Marylou Brogan – Honolulu, Hawaii

caviar pie

8 hard boiled eggs
4 green onions
4 tablespoons mayonnaise
2 jars black lump fish caviar
1/2 pint sour cream

Chop the eggs and 3 green onions and mix with the mayonnaise. Spread on the bottom of a shallow glass dish (8 or 9-inch). Layer the egg mixture with first the caviar, then the sour cream. Decorate the top of the sour cream with the remaining chopped green onion.

…do the layering of this caviar pie just before you serve it. Serve with petit rye bread.

Dale Solheim – Aspen, Colorado

caviar log

1 4-3/4-ounce can liver paté
1 2-ounce jar black caviar
4 3-ounce packages cream cheese
melba toast rounds

Paté, caviar and cheese should be at room temperature. Place cream cheese on wax paper, using paper to roll and shape cheese into a log. Spread evenly with liver paté, then cover with caviar. Lightly cover with clear plastic wrap. Chill at least 1 hour. Serve with melba toast.

...I use Romanoff caviar.

Barbara Bell – Aspen, Colorado

spicy chicken liver paté

1/4 pound bacon
1/4 pound butter
3 medium onions, chopped
1/2 bell pepper
1 pound chicken livers
3 cloves garlic, chopped
1 heaping teaspoon jalapeno peppers,
       chopped
1 teaspoon dry mustard
1 teaspoon salt
1/2 teaspoon black pepper
1/2 teaspoon mace
1/4 teaspoon thyme
1/2 teaspoon powdered cloves
dash of cayenne
1 ounce brandy

In a large skillet, cook bacon until nearly done but not crisp. Add a stick of butter and melt. Add onions, garlic and bell pepper and saute about 3 minutes. Add chicken livers and cook an additional 6 minutes until pink.

In a blender, combine jalapenos with a small amount of the onion and livers from the skillet and blend until thoroughly mixed. Add the balance of the contents from the skillet and blend until smooth. Add salt, pepper and the rest of the spices and blend thoroughly. Deglaze the skillet with brandy, pour into blender, and blend until mixed. Pour into container and chill.

Angus Anderson – Aspen, Colorado

spinach puffs with mustard sauce

2 10-ounce packages frozen, chopped
    spinach
2 cups herb stuffing mix
1 5-ounce wedge Parmesan cheese
1 stick butter
4 small green onions
3 eggs
dash of freshly grated nutmeg
mustard sauce

Thaw the spinach, squeeze dry and put in a large bowl. Crush the stuffing mix and grate the Parmesan cheese. Melt the butter and finely chop the onions. Combine all ingredients except mustard sauce in bowl with spinach and mix well. Shape into 1-inch balls. Cover and refrigerate or freeze until ready to bake.

Preheat oven to 350° Set balls on ungreased baking sheet and bake until golden brown, about 10 to 15 minutes. Serve with mustard sauce. Makes about 70 puffs.

mustard sauce

1/2 cup dry mustard
1/2 cup white vinegar
1/2 cup sugar
1 egg yolk

Combine mustard and vinegar in small bowl. Cover and let stand at room temperature 4 hours. Mix sugar and egg yolk in small saucepan. Add mustard and vinegar mixture and cook over a low heat, stirring constantly, until slightly thickened. Cover and chill. Serve at room temperature.

Bonnie Prior – Honolulu, Hawaii

oysters rockefeller

3 pounds fresh spinach
3/4 pound butter
1/2 onion, minced
4 slices bacon, minced
2 whole pimentos, diced
6 dashes Tabasco
1/4 cup Worcestershire sauce
1 tablespoon msg
3 ounces Pernod
32 freshly shucked oysters – hand picked,
    medium

Wash the spinach and remove the stems. Saute in butter minced onions and minced bacon until slightly brown. Add diced pimentos, spinach and seasonings. Cook until spinach has softened. Add Pernod, and remove from heat.

In the larger bottom shell, make a bed of spinach for the fresh oysters. Sparingly cover oysters with additional spinach mixture. Bake at 450° for 7-8 minutes or until oysters are firm. Top with a traditional sauce Hollandaise. Serves 8.

Rex Chandler – Honolulu, Hawaii

lomi salmon

1 pound salted salmon
5 large ripe tomatoes
1 large onion
3 cubes of ice

Select salmon with thick meat. Soak in boiling water for 10 minutes and drain. If very salty, repeat, but do not let stand as long. Take off skin and free from bones. Break into small pieces, and put into a bowl. Cut up tomatoes and add. Slice and chop onion in small pieces and add. Put the ice in, and squeeze salmon, onions, tomato and ice through the fingers until all are in small pieces. Chill in refrigerator…a little finely cut up green onion will add color.

Lucy Blaisdell – Honolulu, Hawaii

smoked salmon mousse

1/2 pound smoked salmon
juice from 1 lemon
3 tablespoons butter
1 cup sour cream
pepper to taste
1 teaspoon fresh chopped dill

Puree salmon and lemon juice in a blender or food processor. Melt butter and add to salmon in a steady stream while blending. Remove to bowl and fold in sour cream, pepper and chopped dill. Place in serving dish and chill well. Garnish with tiny lemon slices, and sprinkle fresh dill on top.

...dry dill may be substituted but use less.

...serve with dry, crisp toast points or melba toast...this is so easy, and quick to make, it's always a big hit.

Marjorie Wilson – Honolulu, Hawaii

shrimp mousse

1-1/2 envelopes Knox gelatin
1/2 cup water
1 can tomato soup
1 8-ounce package cream cheese
1 cup Miracle Whip
3/4 to 1 pound baby shrimp
3/4 cup minced celery
3/4 cup minced onion
dash of lemon juice

Dissolve gelatin in water. Put soup in double boiler then add gelatin and water mixture. Add cream cheese and whip with an electric beater, as mixture heats. Remove from heat and add Miracle Whip, shrimp, celery, onions, and lemon juice...to taste. Place in mold and refrigerate.

Marjane Wall – San Francisco, California

art's special poki

1 pound ono, or mahi-mahi, or marlin
    (any white fish)
2 limes
2 teaspoons dill weed
1 teaspoon black pepper
1 teaspoon salt
2 teaspoons white vinegar
2 teaspoons oil
1/2 diced onion

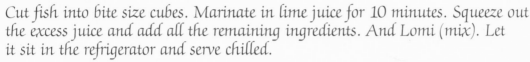

Cut fish into bite size cubes. Marinate in lime juice for 10 minutes. Squeeze out the excess juice and add all the remaining ingredients. And Lomi (mix). Let it sit in the refrigerator and serve chilled.

Dr. Art Kamisugi – Honolulu, Hawaii

crab stuffed snow peas

Cut ends and pull string off snow peas. Boil peas in salted water for one minute. Rinse immediately under cold water. Cut or shred crab into very small pieces. Finely chop celery and onion and mix with crab. Add salt and pepper to taste. Add a small amount of mayonnaise. Slit peas along one side and stuff with mixture.

Misayo Kikuchi – Honolulu, Hawaii

extra special clam dip

3 8-ounce packages cream cheese
8 limes
1-1/2 onions, chopped fine
3 cans minced clams

Soften cream cheese and put in a large bowl, mash with fork. Squeeze juice from limes and add to cream cheese. Add onions and mix. Then add clams together with a little of their juice. Mix all together, using your own judgement of how much clam juice you want so dip is soft, but not too soft. Serves 8.

Carla Beachcomber – Honolulu, Hawaii

tahitian raw fish

white fish (preferably)
rock salt
fresh lime juice
green onions
coconut cream

While white fish is preferable, any big, fresh fish will do. Cut in bite-size pieces. Mix with rock salt and allow to stand 2 to 3 hours until salt permeates fish. Rinse, leaving some salt. Completely cover fish with fresh lime juice. Do not spare the lime juice, as it cooks the fish. Cover and refrigerate overnight. The next day, pour off the lime juice. Cover the fish with coconut cream. Add a generous amount of thinly sliced green onions. Mix well and serve very cold.

Coconut cream – make fresh coconut cream or use frozen coconut milk.

Peg Rowe – Kailua, Hawaii

curried ceviche scallops

1-1/2 pounds bay scallops (raw)
double recipe of basic vinaigrette dressing
3 to 4 tablespoons curry powder
1 to 2 garlic cloves
1/2 inch pieces of fresh ginger
salt
freshly ground pepper

basic vinaigrette dressing

1 cup good quality olive oil
1/4 cup freshly squeezed lemon juice
salt and fresh ground black pepper

Place scallops in a large glass bowl. Combine remaining ingredients in a blender or food processor until thoroughly mixed. Taste and adjust seasonings. Pour over scallops and marinate overnight.

…for the dressing, combine oil and lemon juice, then salt and pepper to taste.

Carl Jerome – Aspen, Colorado
(author of New Recipes for the Cuisinart
with James Beard)

tahitian shrimps

24 medium shrimp – unpeeled,
    frozen raw
1 ounce dry sherry
1 ounce dry vermouth
1/4 teaspoon ajinomoto
1/4 teaspoon white pepper
juice of 1 large lime
1 small clove garlic, minced
4 tablespoons good olive oil
1/2 cup Hawaiian red rock salt – if not
    available – crude white salt
lime wedges

Thoroughly defrost shrimp. In a cup, combine all other ingredients except rock salt and olive oil. Pour olive oil into heavy round omelette skillet and heat until it begins to smoke. Quickly place shrimps in skillet in one layer. Cook 2 minutes on one side then turn and cook 2 minutes on other side. Reduce heat to medium, and slowly shuffle skillet back and forth over flame, at the same time pouring contents of cup over shrimps. Immediately clamp tight lid on skillet and continue shuffling for one minute longer. Then remove lid and sprinkle rock salt over.shrimps, all the while continuing to shuffle skillet, and cook for 1 minute longer – no more. Turn out contents of skillet onto heated platter.

Guests will peel their own shrimp and squeeze a few drops of fresh lime juice over each…provide a steaming, scented towel when they have finished.

Buttered toast and a dry sherry are excellent accompaniments for this pupu.

Remember that the success of this recipe depends upon speed of cooking. This should be not longer than 5 minutes from start to finish.

Carla Beachcomber – Honolulu, Hawaii

coquilles st. jacques

1 pint scallops
2 cups boiling water
1/2 cup butter
1 pound fresh mushrooms
3 tablespoons flour
1/2 teaspoon salt
1/8 teaspoon pepper
1 cup milk
1/2 cup bread crumbs

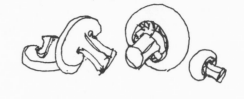

Put scallops in boiling water; simmer 10 minutes. Clean and slice mushrooms. Melt butter and add mushrooms. Brown lightly for 5 minutes. Remove from pan, add flour, salt, pepper and stir until smooth. Slowly add milk. Cook until thickened. Add scallops and mushrooms to sauce. Put into casserole or scallop shells. Top with buttered crumbs. Bake at 350° for 35 minutes.

Marylou Brogan – Honolulu, Hawaii

samosa

2 pounds white salad potatoes
1 package wonton pi (about 40 pieces)
1 teaspoon cumin
1 teaspoon ground coriander
dash of cayenne pepper

1 tablespoon fresh Chinese parsley, chopped
1/2 cup boiled green peas
salt and pepper to taste

Boil potatoes until done. Peel and cut into small cubes. Combine all ingredients in a bowl except wonton. Put 1 of the wonton pi on a cutting board. Put a heaping tablespoon of the potato mixture in the center of the wonton. With your fingertips, apply water on all edges of wonton, fold over the edges and seal. Repeat with remaining pieces. These can be made ahead.

Fry in hot oil until golden brown. Serve with catsup as a dip. Fry only when ready to eat. Serve hot.

…always a big success at my parties.

…available (wonton pi) in the same department of market where Chinese noodles are sold.

Indru Watamull – Honolulu, Hawaii

chipped beef dip

1/4 cup green pepper
1 8-ounce package cream cheese
2 tablespoons milk
1 2-1/2-ounce package chipped beef
2 tablespoons onion flakes
1/2 cup sour cream
1/2 teaspoon garlic salt
1/2 cup pecans
2 tablespoons butter
1/2 teaspoon salt

Finely chop green pepper and mix with cream cheese, milk, chipped beef, onion, sour cream and garlic. In a pan, saute the pecans, butter and salt. Spread pecan mixture over beef mixture and bake at 350° for 20 minutes, or longer if dip has been refrigerated.

Terease Hampton – Ponca City, Oklahoma

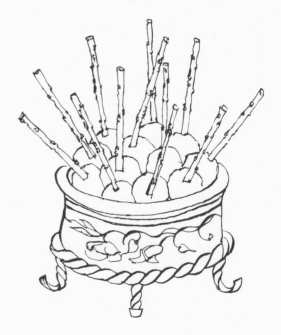

chipped beef balls

1 small jar chipped beef
2 3-ounce packages cream cheese
1 teaspoon horseradish
1 sprig parsley, chopped
3/4 cup grated Parmesan cheese
pretzel sticks

Finely chop beef and mix together with cream cheese, horseradish and parsley. Form into bite size balls and roll in Parmesan cheese. Chill. Just before serving, spear each ball with a pretzel stick. Serves 8.

Betty Perry – Honolulu, Hawaii

hot sausage pick ups

10 ounces sharp cheese, grated
3 cups biscuit mix
1 pound extra hot bulk sausage,
    uncooked (Jimmy Dean, etc.)

Melt cheese over hot water. Add and work in biscuit mix and sausage. Shape into bite-size balls. Bake at 350° for 10 to 15 minutes, until golden brown. Freeze unbaked balls and just take out and bake as needed. When using frozen, bake at 350° for 20 to 25 minutes, on an ungreased sheet.

Jane Armstrong – Dallas, Texas

beth's chili dip

4 pounds ground round
2 large onions
2 large packages Velveeta cheese
1 16-ounce can pork and beans
1/2 can Milnot
3 packages chili mix
2 16-ounce cans hot jalapenos

Saute ground round and onion until brown. Drain and put in a large pan. Melt cheese in a double boiler. Add melted cheese, beans, Milnot and chili mix to meat. Cook over medium heat. Seed and chop jalapenos and add to mixture. Heat thoroughly. Serve in chafing dish with corn chips or taco chips.

Beth Davison – Oklahoma City, Oklahoma

appetizer chicken wings

1/2 cup soy sauce
1/2 cup sake or plum wine
2 tablespoons minced ginger
2 tablespoons minced garlic
2 tablespoons minced scallions
dash of Tabasco
2 tablespoons honey
20 chicken wings
1/2 cup corn meal
1/2 cup Wondra flour
2 tablespoons turmeric
2 tablespoons paprika
1 tablespoon black pepper
1 teaspoon salt

Mix soy sauce, wine, ginger, garlic, scallions, Tabasco and honey to make a marinade. Remove tips and cut joints of chicken wings to make 40 pieces. Pierce chicken wings with fork, place in a bowl and pour marinade over them. Marinate for at least 6 hours. Remove from marinade and pat lightly with a paper towel. Place corn meal, flour, turmeric, paprika, pepper and salt in a plastic bag and shake thoroughly. Then add chicken wings. Shake bag well, until chicken is covered with mixture. Place on a cookie sheet or shallow roasting pan and bake for 1 hour at 350°.

Lilia Lee – Honolulu, Hawaii

diane's japanese chicken

5 pounds chicken thighs
1/2 cup cornstarch
1/2 cup mochiko (glutenous rice flour)
1/2 cup sugar
10 tablespoons soy sauce
1 teaspoon salt
4 eggs, lightly beaten
1/2 cup chopped green onions
garlic to taste
oil for deep fat frying

De-bone chicken. Cut in two to three pieces. Mix together remaining ingredients and marinate chicken. Deep fry until golden brown.

Jody Widner – Honolulu, Hawaii

armenian steak tartar

1 pound or 2 cups lean lamb, or sirloin
1/2 cup chopped parsley
1/2 cup finely chopped onion
2/3 teaspoon salt
cayenne pepper to taste
2 cups fine bulgur (cracked wheat)
1 cup ice water

Grind meat with the metal blade of processor 3 times. Add parsley, onion, salt and pepper. Blend meat with bulgur, using ice water slowly as you knead the meat for approximately 10 minutes in the center of a bowl. Knead until meat and bulgur form a smooth mixture. Shape into small patties, about 25, 1-1/2 inches in diameter. This is about right for hors d'oeuvres. Serve immediately.

You can use some of the leftover vegetables for garnish.

This is called keyma in Armenian – chee kufta in Turkish, meaning raw meat with vegetable mixture.

Ron Krajan – Newport Beach, California

steak tartar

2 pounds ground beef round
3/4 cup finely chopped onion
3/4 cup capers, drained
6 anchovy fillets (finely chopped)
4 egg yolks
1/4 teaspoon finely ground pepper
1/4 cup chopped watercress or parsley
party rye bread or crackers

Grind beef 3 times and put in a large bowl. Add all other ingredients and toss lightly. Mound on a serving platter or mold in a decorative mold and garnish with anchovy fillet strips and capers. Refrigerate 3 to 4 hours before serving. Surround with party rye or crackers. Makes about 20 servings.

Allan J. Feldman – Oklahoma City, Oklahoma

appetizers

appetizer bleu cheese burgers

2 pounds lean ground beef
1/2 cup chopped onion
1 cup soft bread crumbs
1 egg
1 teaspoon salt
2 4-ounce packages chopped bleu cheese crumbles
2 packages small, square party rolls, heated, split
lettuce

Combine meat, onion, bread crumbs, egg and salt; mix lightly. Press meat mixture into 15-1/2 x 10-1/2-inch jelly roll pan to within 1 inch of edge of pan. Bake at 350° for 20 minutes. Drain. Top meat mixture with bleu cheese crumbles. Continue baking until cheese is melted. Cut into 40 squares. Serve on rolls with lettuce.

Sugar and Spice

best ever no bean dip

1 pound Velveeta cheese
1 can chili without beans
1 bunch green onions
1 4-ounce can green chiles
1/4 teaspoon liquid pepper

Chop cheese, onions and chiles. Mix all ingredients together and divide into 2 small ovenproof dishes. Bake at 275° for an hour. Serve with homemade chips.

Linda O'Connor – Honolulu, Hawaii

special mexican chips

Cut up 1 package of corn tortillas into triangular pieces. Fry in small batches in bacon grease. Fry them until crisp. Salt to taste. Delicious!

…the secret of these chips seems to be in using a heavy frying pan. Making the chips in small batches and using only bacon grease, heated so when you add the chips, it foams.

Linda O'Connor – Honolulu, Hawaii

49

chili con queso

1/2 pound Velveeta cheese
1/2 pound sharp cheddar
2 small cans jalapeño peppers
3 large cloves garlic
4 whole canned tomatoes, drained
    and squeezed

Grate cheese. Remove seed – chop peppers fine. Chop garlic and tomatoes. Layer all ingredients in a casserole. Do not stir. Bake at 350° for 30 minutes, uncovered. Let stand 15 minutes before serving.

Glenda Pell – Honolulu, Hawaii

super nachos

1 10-ounce can refried beans
1 pound ground beef
1 onion, chopped
1 can chopped green chiles
1/2 pound grated jack cheese
3 tablespoons taco sauce, red or green
1 green onion, chopped
1 small can olives, chopped
1 small carton sour cream
1 avocado for guacamole
tortilla chips

Saute onion and ground beef together until browned. Drain fat. Spread beans on bottom of an oven-proof baking dish. Cover with beef and onion mixture. Layer chiles over this and top with grated cheese. Drizzle taco sauce all over cheese and bake in a pre-heated oven at 350° until cheese bubbles. Approximately 20 minutes. Meanwhile, make guacamole and chill.

Remove from oven and sprinkle green onion and olives all over. Spread guacamole around the center, leaving at least a one-inch border of cheese-meat mixture showing. Top this with sour cream, leaving some of the guacamole showing. Add more olives and green onion all over the top for decoration.

Take any strong corn or tortilla chips and arrange around the edge of the dish, petal shape, and serve.

…this is a very colorful appetizer and is usually devoured within minutes.

Valerie Davis – Honolulu, Hawaii

dill

dill

possible Egyptian origin...its name is derived from the Norwegian word dilla meaning "to lull" and has a medicinal history from Greek and Roman times...in the early days of the American colonies, dill served as a pacifier that youngsters munched on when restless and hungry in church, listening to those interminable sermons.

Soups

cold caviar consomme

3 envelopes gelatin
6 cups chicken broth
6 teaspoons cognac
3 jars red caviar

condiments:

1 onion (minced)
2 hard boiled eggs (chopped)
1 cup sour cream

Prepare chicken consomme either by making your own clarified chicken stock or by using canned chicken stock adding unflavored gelatin in the following proportions.

1 envelope of gelatin for each 3 cups of liquid. Sprinkle 3 envelopes of gelatin into 1-1/2 cups of cold broth and let soften for 3 to 4 minutes. Blend mixture into remaining stock, adding cognac and stir over moderate heat for several minutes until the gelatin has completely dissolved. Chill. After consomme has jelled, blend in red caviar with a fork to distribute evenly. Divide into individual servings and top each serving with eggs, onion and a tablespoon of sour cream.
Serve with Aquavit!

Max H. Davis – Honolulu, Hawaii

gazpacho blanco

4 medium cucumbers
2-1/2 cups chicken broth
2 cups plain yogurt
3 tablespoons white wine vinegar
1-1/2 teaspoons salt
1 medium clove garlic
1 tomato
3 green onions

Peel cucumbers and chop coarsely. Whirl cucumber and 1 cup broth in blender for just a moment, leaving bits of cucumber visible. Stir in remaining broth, vinegar, yogurt, salt and minced garlic. Whirl again to blend. Chill and garnish with chopped tomatoes and green onion. Serves 4-6.

Ruth Stebbins – Honolulu, Hawaii

gazpacho for 30

15 to 18 cloves garlic
1 tablespoon salt
5 pounds tomatoes, skinned
1/2 cup olive oil
1 onion
1/3 cup wine vinegar
4 green peppers (1 to 1-1/4 pounds)
3 cucumbers (2 to 2-1/4 pounds)
2 46-ounce cans tomato juice

Peel garlic and grind together with salt in a food processor to make a puree. Set aside. Process half of the tomatoes to a smooth consistency; slowly add 1/4 cup of the olive oil, until well blended. Repeat process with remaining tomatoes and olive oil. Grind onions and mix with wine vinegar. Set aside. Grind remaining vegetables and stir into tomatoes. Add onion, garlic and juice. Chill well. Garnish with Chinese parsley, if desired. Add cubed tomatoes, cucumbers and green peppers to individual bowls. Makes 30 7-ounce servings.

Barbara Gray – Honolulu, Hawaii

cold carrot soup

3 tablespoons butter
1-1/2 cups onion
1 celery stalk, leaves finely
    chopped
1-1/2 pounds carrots
2 medium potatoes
1 teaspoon sugar
1 teaspoon dried dill
3 cups chicken broth
1 cup milk
1 cup heavy cream
pinch of cayenne
salt and white pepper
chopped fresh parsley for garnish

Melt butter, add finely chopped onion and celery and saute until onion is translucent. Cut carrots into 1/4-inch rounds, peel and dice potatoes and add to onions
with sugar, dill, and broth. Cook, covered, on low heat for 25 minutes, cool slightly
and puree in processor about 1/4 mixture at a time. Cover and chill (can also be
frozen at this point). Just before serving add milk, cream, cayenne, salt and pepper.

Glenda Pell – Honolulu, Hawaii

cantaloupe soup

4 small, ripe cantaloupes
1 6-ounce can frozen orange juice
1 cup honey (to taste)
1 cup whipping cream
1/2 cup brandy
fresh mint garnish

Peel and seed cantaloupes. In a food processor combine first 5 ingredients. Blend
until smooth. Make in two batches. Adjust taste. Chill. When serving, garnish with
mint. Serves 8.

Dale Solheim – Aspen, Colorado

blender borsht

1-1/2 to 1-2/3 cups sliced beets
    (16-ounce can)
1/2 cup beet juice from can
3/4 cup chicken broth
1 teaspoon lemon juice
1 rounded teaspoon chopped onion
1/2 teaspoon salt
2 tablespoons sour cream

Puree beets, juice, chicken broth, lemon juice, onion and salt in a blender until smooth. Reserve sour cream. Chill several hours or overnight to develop flavor. Garnish with sour cream and chopped chives. Serves 4.

Sugar and Spice

cold cream of cucumber soup

2-1/2 pounds cucumbers
1/2 cup minced shallots or onions
3 tablespoons butter
6 cups light chicken stock
1-1/2 teaspoons vinegar
1 teaspoon dill weed
1 cup sour cream
1/2 teaspoon fresh or dried dill
salt and white pepper to taste

Peel and cut cucumbers into chunks. Cook shallots in butter slowly until tender but not brown. Add cucumber, chicken stock, vinegar and dill. Bring to a boil, then simmer for 25 minutes. Puree, then return soup to saucepan. Add salt and pepper to taste. When cool, add sour cream and refrigerate until very cold – about 2 hours. Sprinkle with dill and serve.

Peggy Ann Lehmkuhl – Honolulu, Hawaii

56

cold cucumber and watercress soup

4 cucumbers
2 shallots or 1 medium onion
7 cups chicken stock
1/4 cup butter
2 tablespoons flour
salt and pepper to taste
3 egg yolks
1/2 cup heavy cream

garnish

1 cup watercress leaves
1/4 cup whipping cream

Peel and chop the cucumbers and finely chop onion or shallots. Combine these in a heavy pan with the chicken stock and simmer for 15 - 20 minutes. When soft, puree in a blender or food processor. Strain the mixture if you wish a smooth texture. In the same pan, melt the butter and combine with the flour and cook until the flour is straw colored. Carefully return the puree to the flour mixture and simmer for 2 to 3 minutes after the mixture returns to a boil. Add the seasonings.

Mix the egg yolks and cream together. Add a small amount of the hot puree to the eggs and slowly add to the hot puree in the pan. Reheat very carefully until slightly thickened. Do not allow to boil. Chill covered with a plastic wrap so that a skin will not form.

When ready to serve, whip the cream to hold soft peaks. Place a small amount on the top of each serving and sprinkle the watercress on top.

Lavonne Tollerud – Honolulu, Hawaii

lentil mushroom soup

1-1/2 quarts chicken broth
2 cups lentils, washed
1 large onion, chopped
1/2 pound mushrooms, sliced
1 teaspoon dried basil
1/2 teaspoon salt
2 stalks celery with tops,
    chopped
2 carrots, sliced
1 1-pound can stewed tomatoes
1/4 can olive oil
2 tablespoons vinegar

Bring stock to a boil and slowly add lentils. Reduce heat to a simmer, and cook 1/2 to 1 hour. Meanwhile, saute onion, mushrooms, and basil in oil. Combine all ingredients, except vinegar, and cook 1 more hour or until lentils are tender. Add vinegar before serving. Add salt and pepper to taste. Serves 4 well as a dinner with a green salad.

Good when made ahead so flavors meld. Can also be served over brown rice.

Virginia Stringer – Honolulu, Hawaii

fresh mushroom soup

1 8-ounce box mushrooms,
    stems separated from caps
5 tablespoons butter
3 heaping tablespoons flour
1 14-1/2 ounce can chicken broth
2 cups milk
1/4 cup crème fraiche
salt and pepper to taste

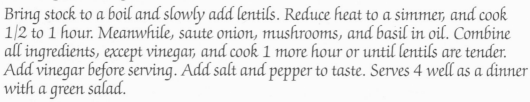

Chop mushroom stems and a few caps in a food processor. Saute in butter. Add flour and stir. Add broth and heat until simmering. Add milk and the rest of the mushrooms, which have been chopped in the food processor. Season with salt and pepper. Cook until hot, add crème fraiche.

Marjorie Wilson – Honolulu, Hawaii

mexican oatmeal soup

1-1/3 cups rolled oats
8 tablespoons butter
1 large onion, chopped
3 large cloves garlic, crushed
2 large tomatoes, chopped
6 cups chicken broth
1 teaspoon salt

Toast oats in a large heavy skillet over medium heat, stirring frequently until browned but not burned. Watch carefully as they do burn if you don't keep tossing them. Place oats in a bowl and set aside. Melt butter in skillet, add onions, garlic, tomatoes, chicken broth, salt, and browned oats. Boil for 6 minutes over medium heat. Serve hot. Serves 8.

…also good the next day, reheated.
…I use Quaker Old-fashioned oats, just do not buy the quick cooking kind.

…unbelievably delicious!

Linda Janovic – New York, New York

split pea soup

1 pound (2-1/4 cups) green split peas
1 meaty ham bone
1-1/2 cups sliced onion
1 teaspoon salt
1 cup diced carrots
1/2 teaspoon pepper
1/4 teaspoon marjoram
1 cup diced celery

Cover peas with 2 quarts cold water and soak overnight. Add ham bone, onion and seasonings. Bring to a boil, reduce heat and simmer (not boiling) 1-1/2 hours, stirring occasionally. Remove bone, cut off meat and dice, return meat to soup. Add vegetables, cook slowly, 30 to 40 minutes, uncovered. Salt to taste.

Barbara Bell – Aspen, Colorado

escargot soup

1 small can snails
4 tablespoons unsalted butter
4 shallots, minced
6 chantarelle mushrooms, minced
2 cloves garlic, minced
3 tablespoons minced parsley
1-1/2 quarts beef stock
1/2 cup heavy cream
2 tablespoons Worcestershire sauce
salt and freshly ground white pepper
    to taste
3 tablespoons Pernod liqueur
1-1/2 cups whipped cream
1/2 teaspoon curry powder
2 egg whites beaten stiff

Drain canned snails and mince very fine. Set aside. In a heavy saucepan, melt butter. Add shallots and cook until limp. Add mushrooms, garlic and half of the chopped parsley. Saute 5 minutes while stirring with a wooden spoon. Add stock and cream and cook on low heat for 15 minutes, then strain through sieve into a bowl, pressing residue through sieve with a wooden spoon.

Return to saucepan and add snails, Worcestershire sauce, salt and pepper, remainder of parsley and Pernod. Cover and simmer for 10 minutes.

Bring soup to a boil and pour into ovenproof bowls. Fold beaten egg whites into whipped cream; add curry, salt and pepper to taste. Top each bowl with this mixture and place under broiler for a few minutes until cream is slightly brown. Serve immediately.

Jorgen Skov – Honolulu, Hawaii

jerry's california seafood bisque

3/4 to 1 pound shrimp or lobster meat
    (cooked)
1 onion, diced
2 tablespoons butter
3 tablespoons flour
2 cups milk
2 cups chicken broth
3/4 can tomato paste
cayenne pepper, nutmeg, Spike,
    white pepper, marjoram
1/2 cup light cream
6-8 teaspoons sherry
dried parsley

To cook shrimp, peel and devein, and put in a pot of boiling water. Cook for 3 minutes. Remove and run under cold water to stop cooking. Set aside. Dice and cook onion in butter until soft. Add flour and stir. Scald milk and add to flour and butter mixture, gradually add chicken broth. Add tomato paste by the spoonful. Cook until slightly thick. Season with cayenne pepper, nutmeg, Spike, white pepper, marjoram and your imagination.

Scald cream and add alternately with sherry. Taste; if necessary, add more. Add dried or fresh chopped parsley. Add shrimp and any other shellfish you wish. Lobster meat is especially delectable in this soup. Serve hot with a piece of garlic bread…be prepared to do a lot of lip-licking!

                           Jerry Goldman – Los Angeles, California

crab bisque ernie coker

1/2 stick butter
1/2 cup chopped green onion
1/3 cup flour
1 quart milk
1 cup light cream
1/3 pound crab

Melt butter in a pan that will hold at least 2 quarts. Saute chopped green onion and when brown, add flour to make a roux. Very slowly, add heated milk, a little at a time, stirring constantly. Add cream. Add crab and season with white pepper and Lawry's seasoning salt to taste.

…Gulf Coast blue crabs recommended, use only the back fin.

                           Scott Van de Mark – Aspen, Colorado

clam chowder

1-1/2 cups vegetable oil
2 cups flour
3/4 pound bacon, diced
1 medium onion, diced
1 cup celery, diced
1 cup leeks, diced
1 12-16 ounce can tomatoes
    drained and diced

46 ounces chopped clams
46 ounces clam juice
3 cups water
1-3/4 cups half & half
3 medium russet potatoes, diced
1 tablespoon salt
1 tablespoon pepper

Heat oil in a pan and slowly stir in flour. Mix until it is smooth. This mixture is called roux. Set aside. Cook bacon until crisp in a pot large enough to hold all ingredients. Add onions, celery, leeks and tomatoes and stir fry for a few minutes. Add clams, clam juice, and water. Bring to a boil. Add roux to thicken, stirring in salt and pepper. (If recipe is prepared in advance to reheat and serve later, do not precook potatoes. They will cook sufficiently during reheating.)

Serves 16.

Nick Nickolas – Nick's Fishmarket
Chicago and Houston

vichyssoise supreme

3 cups water
1/4 cup chopped parsley
2 tablespoons butter
1/8 teaspoon pepper
1 envelope instant potato flakes
1 medium onion, chopped
4 chicken bouillon cubes
1 teaspoon salt
3 cups half and half

In a large saucepan, combine water, onion, parsley, bouillon cubes, butter and seasonings, and bring to a boil. Stir and cover, simmer until onions are tender, about 10 to 12 minutes. Add half and half and bring to boiling point but do not boil. Remove from heat and stir in potato flakes. Let stand for 3 minutes. Chill well. Garnish with chopped chives. Makes about 6 cups.

…this is Rod's favorite.

Sharon McPhee – Honolulu, Hawaii

pumpkin soup

1 small pumpkin
1 pound 12 ounce gruyere cheese
1 pound (approximate) thinly sliced
    bread (toasted)
1-1/2 cups heavy cream
salt, pepper
3/4 teaspoon nutmeg

Choose a small to medium pumpkin that will fit into your oven. Remove top and set aside. Remove all the seeds and stringy pulp. Dry and season inside of pumpkin with salt and pepper. Fill pumpkin to 3/4 full with alternating layers of toast and very thin strips of cheese, seasoning with salt and quite a bit of pepper.

Replace pumpkin top and place in slow to moderate oven (310°) for about 3 hours, although cooking time depends on size and age of pumpkin. When pumpkin gets a nice bronze color and begins to soften, remove top and add cream into which you have stirred nutmeg. The pumpkin itself will now serve as a tureen. Serve each guest by scooping portions of softened pumpkin with a ladleful of the soup inside. You might want to add more cream for a larger pumpkin.

This is such a rich and filling soup that you may only want a plain green salad and possibly fruit. This soup is excellent served cold the next day.

Rainee Barkhorn – Honolulu, Hawaii

crab bisque

2 tablespoons butter
1 cup minced celery
2 packages (1 ounce each) white
    sauce mix
2 cups half and half
1 13-3/4-ounce can chicken broth
1/3 cup dry sherry
2 cans crabmeat (drained at 5 ounces
    each) and flaked
salt and pepper to taste
pats of butter

In a saucepan, melt butter and saute celery for 5 minutes, or until soft. Stir in sauce mix. Gradually stir in half and half and chicken broth. Add sherry. Stir over low heat until bubbling and thickens slightly. Stir in crabmeat. Simmer for 1 to 2 minutes. Add salt and pepper.   rve in bowls. Top with pats of butter.

Jayne Black – Aspen, Colorado

carol's cioppino

1 onion
1 green pepper
1/2 cup celery
1 carrot
3 cloves garlic
3 tablespoons olive oil
2 1-pound cans tomatoes
1 8-ounce can tomato sauce
1 bay leaf
1 teaspoon salt
1 teaspoon pepper
1 pound halibut
1 dozen clams
1 8-ounce package shrimp
1-1/2 cups white wine

Chop onion, green pepper, and celery; slice carrot, saute these with garlic in olive oil. Add tomatoes, sauce, and bay leaf. Season with salt and pepper. Place all these ingredients in a pot and boil for 2 hours. Remove bay leaf, stir in wine and add fish, simmer for 15 minutes. When serving, top with parsley. Serves 8.

Carol Euster Fuller – Aspen, Colorado

buzz's cioppino

7 large round onions
8 large bell peppers
1 medium bunch parsley
10 cloves garlic
4 bay leaves
4 cloves
1/2 cup salad oil
1 #10 can diced tomatoes
1 quart water
1 quart red wine
1 16-ounce can tomato paste
15 ounces sliced mushrooms
1 pound clams
1 pound crab
1 pound scallops
1 pound shrimp
3-4 ounces white fish meat
additional seafood – optional

Mince onions, peppers, parsley, and cloves of garlic and saute with bay leaves and cloves in 1/2 cup salad oil until clear. Add tomatoes, water, red wine and tomato paste and boil gently for 1 hour covered, stirring occasionally. Add mushrooms. About 15 minutes before serving, add remaining seafood, simmer and serve. If stew is too thick, add more water. Serve with garlic bread and tossed salad. Serves 15 or more.

Bobbie Lou Schneider,
Buzz's Steak House – Honolulu, Hawaii

turkey soup with quenelles

3/4 pound boneless turkey breast meat
3 egg whites
1-1/2 cups heavy cream, not
    ultra pasteurized if possible
4 or 5 sprigs fresh, curly parsley
4 or 5 sprigs fresh coriander
1 tablespoon tarragon
5 quarts turkey soup or broth
1 dozen egg whites with their shells
salt
freshly ground pepper
2 quarts chicken broth
8-ounce package of bean threads

Remove skin from turkey and cut into 5 or 6 chunks. In the beaker of a food pro-cessor fitted with metal chopping blade, process the turkey until very smooth, approximately 20 seconds. Add 3 egg whites and process until thoroughly blended. With the machine still running, gradually pour in the cream, and process for 1 minute. Add fresh herbs and process just long enough for herbs to be chopped up. Season with salt and pepper, to taste…it is all right to taste raw turkey. Transfer this quenelle mixture to a bowl and cover and refrigerate 2 hours.

Final preparations…place turkey soup in a very large pot over medium high heat. While the soup is heating, place the dozen egg whites in a large bowl with their shells and beat with a wire whisk until lightly frothy on top and egg shells are well crumbled. When soup is almost at a boil, add egg whites and shells and stir with a whisk until mixture comes to a boil and performs magic. You will now have a sparkling, golden soup with a "muck" of egg all over the top of it. (The egg shells and whites have drawn out all of the impurities from the soup, producing an elegant clarified consomme of turkey.) Strain carefully through cheesecloth. Place in a clean pot for final cooking.

To cook quenelles…heat chicken broth in a large saute pan until just beginning to boil.

Using two teaspoons, drop ball size portions of quenelle mixture into the stock. Cook for 1 minute then gently roll over on the other side to cook for 1/2 minute. Remove one quenelle to test for doneness. Be sure there is no pinkish color inside. Immediately transfer quenelles to a cold plate. Bring golden consomme to a full boil, add bean thread and quenelles, serve immediately.

…this recipe was originally created by international food authority and restaurant consultant Barbara Kofka for James Beard's 79th birthday party. Ms. Kofka's natural elegant style is reflected in this superb soup. The recipe was modified by Ms. Kofka's friend and co-worker Carl Jerome for a party at Sally Goldman's to celebrate Winterskol in Aspen.

Carl Jerome – Aspen, Colorado

parsley

parsley

Mediterranean origin…its history entwined
in legend, parsley was said to be the food
which made the steeds of the Greek gods
fleet of foot and spirited…in medieval
England, parsley was strongly associated
with the rituals of black magic…of more
practical use to the American Indians,
parsley roots were roasted and ground
into flour.

Salads

molded cranberry salad

1 package cranberries
1 large unpeeled navel orange
1 cup chopped pecans
1-1/2 cups sugar
1 package lemon jello

Grind cranberries and orange in food grinder, add sugar and pecans. Then dissolve lemon jello in water. Fold the cranberry mixture into the jello, pour into mold and refrigerate.

Pearl J. Marks – Ponca City, Oklahoma

christmas cranberry salad

3 cups cranberries
1 cup water
1-1/4 cup sugar
1 package cherry jello
1 envelope unflavored gelatin
1-1/2 cup seedless grapes
1 small can crushed pineapple

dressing

4 ounces miniature marshmallows
1 3-ounce package cream cheese
1/2 pint heavy cream

Boil cranberries in 1 cup water with sugar until cranberries snap. Dissolve cherry jello and unflavored gelatin in 1/2 cup cold water. Add boiled cranberries, sugar and water to gelatins. Cool. Cut grapes in halves, drain pineapple and add to berry mixture. Pour into an 8-inch ring mold. Refrigerate.

For dressing, mix all ingredients together and refrigerate several hours. Beat just before serving.

Unmold salad on round silver platter. Surround with lettuce. Place dressing in a small bowl in center of mold.

Margie Pietsch – Honolulu, Hawaii

frozen pineapple salad

1 15-ounce can crushed pineapple
1 3-ounce package Philadelphia Brand
    cream cheese
1 cup miniature marshmallows
1/2 cup Miracle Whip salad dressing
1/2 pint whipping cream, whipped

Mix pineapple and cream cheese until creamy. Add marshmallows and Miracle Whip. Fold all these ingredients into the whipped cream. Place in a 9-inch square pan or in a loaf pan and freeze.

Iris Widner – Honolulu, Hawaii

pineapple lime jello salad

1 package lime jello
1 15-ounce can crushed pineapple,
    undrained
1 3-ounce package Philadelphia Brand
    cream cheese
1 3-ounce package pimento cream cheese
1/2 small green pepper, chopped finely
1/2 cup chopped pecans
1 tablespoon Worcestershire sauce

Dissolve jello in 1 cup boiling water and juice from pineapple. Cream cheeses with the pineapple. Add all ingredients to dissolved jello. Pour into a mold and refrigerate until molded.

Iris Widner – Honolulu, Hawaii

velvet salad

1 package lemon jello
2 cups hot water
1 small package marshmallows
1 small can crushed pineapple
1 package (3 ounces) Philadelphia
    cream cheese
1 cup mayonnaise
1 cup whipped cream
1 3-ounce package raspberry jello
1-1/4 cups hot water

Dissolve lemon jello in hot water (1 cup). Dissolve marshmallows in 1 cup hot water also. Mix cream cheese with pineapple. Add mayonnaise and when above ingredients are cooled enough, add whipped cream and place in a baking dish 10 x 12 inches. Let congeal. Take raspberry jello and dissolve into 1-1/4 cups hot water. When cool, add as a topping to the salad.

Serves 15. This should be made the day before serving.

Dorothy Paynter Crawford – Ponca City, Oklahoma

mandarin orange salad

1/2 head lettuce, shredded
1 tablespoon minced parsley
1 11-ounce can mandarin oranges,
     drained
1 cup chopped celery
2 green onions, sliced

dressing

1/2 teaspoon salt
1/4 teaspoon Tabasco sauce
2 tablespoons tarragon vinegar
1/4 cup toasted almonds
dash of ground pepper
2 tablespoons sugar
1/4 cup salad oil

Combine dressing ingredients in a jar and mix well. Toss with greens and fruit.
Serves 4.

Gail Farden – Honolulu, Hawaii

new zealand salad

1 head lettuce and…all these good things:

bananas, strawberries, pineapple, oranges, apples, onions, cheese, dates, celery
…tossed together.

Squeeze the juice of 3 lemons over salad and mix well. Top with plenty of crispy
chow mein noodles…a dieter's delight.

Gail Farden – Honolulu, Hawaii

universal salad

2 cans French style green beans, drained
1 can peas, drained
1 can Chinese vegetables, drained
1 can water chestnuts, drained, cut up
1 cup celery, cut into small pieces
1 onion, thinly sliced
1 teaspoon salt
1 teaspoon pepper
1 cup vinegar
1 cup sugar

Mix vinegar and sugar together and let stand to dissolve sugar. Mix all ingredients in a large bowl. Let set for 2 days. The salad will keep 3 weeks in a tight container in the refrigerator.

Dorothy Souligny – Ponca City, Oklahoma

peach's tomato aspic

1/2 cup water
2 envelopes gelatin
4 cups tomato juice
1/2 large onion, cut up in 3 parts
1-1/2 bay leaves
1/2 teaspoon ground cloves
1/2 teaspoon celery salt
1/2 teaspoon dry mustard

In a bowl, soften gelatin in water and set aside. Cook all the other ingredients together, bringing them to a boil and then simmer for about 15 minutes. Strain into a mold* and mix in gelatin. Let stand for a while until lukewarm and add 4 tablespoons lemon juice. Stir well. Refrigerate 4 to 5 hours or overnight. Lower mold into tepid water before unmolding. Homemade mayonnaise (a must) in the center. Decorate with capers and watercress.

*put empty mold in water (and dry) right before filling.

Linda Janovic – New York, New York

nine day coleslaw

3 pounds cabbage
1 package green onions
1 green bell pepper
4 carrots
2 cups sugar
1 tablespoon salt
1 cup salad oil
1 cup vinegar
1 tablespoon celery seed

Finely chop cabbage. Slice green onions very thin. Chop bell pepper and coarsely grate carrots. Mix together and cover with sugar. Let stand for 10 minutes. Boil the vinegar, oil, celery seed and salt. Pour over the cabbage immediately, turn to coat and chill. It is supposed to keep for 9 days. Red cabbage can also be used.

Maxine Van Winkle Treat – Santa Cruz, California

jerry's 'even popeye would flip' spinach salad

1 egg
2 tablespoons grated fresh Parmesan
    cheese
3 tablespoons lemon juice
1 tablespoon Worcestershire sauce
mushrooms, sliced thin
1 teaspoon Dijon mustard
1 teaspoon honey
1/4 cup oil
2 hard cooked eggs, chopped
seasonings...rosemary, oregano,
    tarragon...etc.

Beat the egg and combine with cheese, seasonings of your choice, mustard, lemon juice, Worcestershire sauce and honey, beat well. Add oil and beat. Refrigerate.

Wash a big bunch of spinach and chill. When ready to serve, put spinach in a salad bowl. Add mushrooms and dressing and toss well. Sprinkle eggs and optional bacon over top.

Jerry Goldman – Los Angeles, California

fresh spinach salad

1-pound fresh spinach
1 pound bacon
2 teaspoons sugar
6 hard boiled eggs
3 heads Bibb lettuce
1 10-ounce package frozen peas
1 onion
1/2 pint mayonnaise
1/2 pint Miracle Whip salad dressing
1 cup Swiss cheese, grated

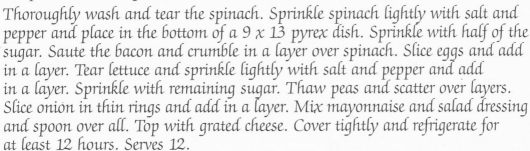

Thoroughly wash and tear the spinach. Sprinkle spinach lightly with salt and pepper and place in the bottom of a 9 x 13 pyrex dish. Sprinkle with half of the sugar. Saute the bacon and crumble in a layer over spinach. Slice eggs and add in a layer. Tear lettuce and sprinkle lightly with salt and pepper and add in a layer. Sprinkle with remaining sugar. Thaw peas and scatter over layers. Slice onion in thin rings and add in a layer. Mix mayonnaise and salad dressing and spoon over all. Top with grated cheese. Cover tightly and refrigerate for at least 12 hours. Serves 12.

Rosemary Paris – Ponca City, Oklahoma

avocado rice salad

1 6-ounce package pre-cooked rice
1/2 cup slivered green peppers
1 4-ounce jar pimentos
1/4 cup chopped parsley
3 tablespoons oil and vinegar dressing
1 ripe avocado, chilled

Cook rice according to the label directions; add green peppers, sliced and drained pimentos and parsley. While still hot, toss in oil and vinegar dressing. Chill thoroughly. Just before serving, add avocado cut in bite size pieces, toss lightly. This can be made ahead of time, except for avocado…morning or day before.

Vera Parkinson – Ponca City, Oklahoma

pea salad

1 package petit pois, frozen peas
   (do not thaw)
1 can smokehouse almonds
1 bunch green onions
approximately 1/2 to 1 cup mayonnaise
1 to 2 teaspoons curry powder
1 can water chestnuts

Grind almonds in a food processor until coarsely ground. Chop the green onions and water chestnuts finely. In a large bowl, add all the ingredients. Keep adding mayonnaise to hold the ingredients together, but not to saturate. Keep it slightly dry. Leave for several hours or overnight in refrigerator. Check to see how taste is. Add more mayonnaise or curry as needed. Serve on mounds of lettuce, in lettuce cups or in 1/2 papaya or fancy cantaloupe.

Lynda Brennan – Honolulu, Hawaii

artichoke rice salad

1 package chicken-flavored rice mix
2 green onions
1/2 green pepper
8 green olives
2 jars marinated artichoke hearts
1/4 teaspoon curry powder
1/3 cup mayonnaise
tomatoes, chopped (optional)

Chop onions, pepper and olive. Cook rice according to package directions but omit the butter. Cool until room temperature. Add artichokes (set aside marinade), add other ingredients. Mix marinade with curry powder and mayonnaise. Mix until smooth. Add rice mixture and mix lightly.

…I suggest using Rice-a-Roni.

…for more rice, add another box. It won't lose flavor.

Alice Mires – Phoenix, Arizona

tabbouleh

1 cup cracked bulgur wheat
2 cups boiling water
1/2 cup vegetable oil
1/2 cup or more fresh lemon juice
2 teaspoons salt
1 teaspoon pepper
1/2 cup chopped parsley
3 tablespoons fresh mint
    or 2 teaspoons dry
1 bunch green onions, finely chopped
2 tomatoes, diced finely

Place wheat in a bowl and pour boiling water over it. Let stand 1 hour then drain. Place back in bowl. Add all ingredients and mix. Chill for 2 hours. Serve with romaine leaves, whole, which you use as a dip.

Rainee Barkhorn – Honolulu, Hawaii

cucumbers in sour cream

1 large cucumber
1 cup sour cream
2 tablespoons green onion, chopped
thin slices of Maui onion
3 tablespoons vinegar
1/4 teaspoon salt
1/8 teaspoon white pepper

Slice cucumbers in thin slices, add the other ingredients and refrigerate for an hour or so.

Lavonne Tollerud – Honolulu, Hawaii

stacy's pasta salad

1 package vermicelli
1 cup sunflower seed oil
1/2 cup lemon juice
1 tablespoon "Accent"
1/2 cup chopped celery
1/2 cup chopped green pepper
1/2 cup chopped onion
1 small jar chopped pimento
1 small can ripe olives (chopped)
salt and mayonnaise to taste

Cook the vermicelli according to package directions and drain in cold water. Mix the oil, lemon juice and Accent with the pasta and refrigerate overnight. Before serving, add the remaining ingredients.

…to make an entree, I add 1 can sliced water chestnuts, 2 cans drained shrimp or diced cooked chicken and 1/2 cup creamy French dressing.

Beth Davison – Oklahoma City, Oklahoma

cucumbers with feta cheese

3 plump cucumbers, about 8 inches long
1/2 cup feta cheese, crumbled
1/4 cup mayonnaise
1/4 teaspoon lemon juice
1/4 teaspoon Worcestershire sauce
1/2 teaspoon dill weed
dash of garlic salt and pepper

Wash cucumbers and trim ends. Core and stand on end to drain. Mash remaining ingredients together. Stuff cucumbers and refrigerate for a few hours. Slice and serve.

Phyllis Jo Sullivan – Honolulu, Hawaii

tomato mozzarella salad

2 firm tomatoes
4 thin slices mozzarella cheese

watercress dressing

1 cup watercress leaves (no stems)
3/4 cup olive oil
1 shallot, peeled
juice from 2 lemons
paprika
fresh, coarse black pepper

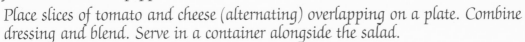

Place slices of tomato and cheese (alternating) overlapping on a plate. Combine dressing and blend. Serve in a container alongside the salad.

Ricki Cassiday – Honolulu, Hawaii

fabulous chicken salad

4 cups cooked chicken breasts
3/4 pound green grapes
1 can water chestnuts
1-1/2 cups pecans
1-1/2 cups celery
2 cups mayonnaise
4 tablespoons red wine vinegar
3 tablespoons soy sauce
1/2 cup minced onion
2 teaspoons curry powder
1-1/2 tablespoons candied ginger

Cube chicken meat and place in a large bowl. Add halved green grapes, sliced water chestnuts, pecans and coarsely chopped celery. In a separate bowl, combine the mayonnaise, vinegar, soy sauce, minced onion, curry powder and chopped ginger. Let this mixture stand for 1 hour, then combine with the chicken. Salad should be chilled for at least 1 hour before serving. Can be served in papaya, cantaloupe or avocado.

Louise N. Feldman – Oklahoma City, Oklahoma

hot chicken salad

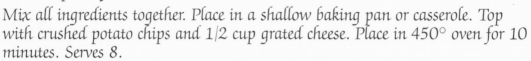

2 cups cubed chicken, cooked
2 cups celery, chopped fine
1/2 teaspoon salt
1/2 teaspoon monosodium glutamate
1/4 teaspoon tarragon
2 tablespoons grated onion
2 tablespoons lemon juice
1-1/2 cups mayonnaise

Mix all ingredients together. Place in a shallow baking pan or casserole. Top with crushed potato chips and 1/2 cup grated cheese. Place in 450° oven for 10 minutes. Serves 8.

…Hellmann's or Best Foods mayonnaise is suggested.

Terease Hampton – Ponca City, Oklahoma

oriental chicken salad

Amounts are not given, so you can vary to suit your taste.
chicken, small julienne strips
carrot, cut in very thin match sticks
cucumber, seeded and cut in very thin match sticks
green onion, sliced in rounds
chopped candied ginger

dressing

1/2 cup Wesson oil
1/4 cup white vinegar
1/4 cup soy sauce
2-3 tablespoons sugar
ginger powder to taste

Mix chicken, carrot and cucumber. Arrange on small plates. Sprinkle green onion and ginger on top. Combine dressing ingredients and spoon 2 tablespoons dressing over each serving.

Marjorie Wilson – Honolulu, Hawaii

chinese chicken salad

1 or 2 chicken breasts
1 can fried noodles
1 bag Fritos
1 head lettuce
4 stalks green onion
4 tablespoons almonds
4 tablespoons sesame seeds

dressing

2 tablespoons sugar
1 teaspoon salt
1 teaspoon msg
1/2 teaspoon pepper
1 tablespoon sesame oil
3 tablespoons white vinegar
1/4 cup salad oil

Boil chicken in salted water, cool and shred. Crush Fritos, shred lettuce, chop green onions and almonds, toast sesame seeds. Mix dressing ingredients together. Toss all ingredients and pour dressing over salad. Garnish with Chinese parsley.

Judy Richardson – Kailua, Hawaii

taco salad

1-1/2 pounds ground beef
1 package taco seasoning
1 small can green chilies
dash of Tabasco
1 large can kidney beans
2 heads romaine lettuce
3 avocados
1 red onion
3 tomatoes (sliced)
1/2 pound cheddar cheese
1 bag crushed tortilla chips

Brown hamburger with taco seasoning, green chilies and Tabasco. Reduce heat and add kidney beans, cooking until beans are heated. Wash lettuce and tear into small pieces. Place lettuce, sliced avocados, chopped onion and chopped tomatoes in salad bowl. Add hot hamburger mixture and cover with grated cheese and crushed chips. Toss and serve immediately.

Brenda Lennox and Helen Skov – Honolulu, Hawaii

taco-less taco salad

1 pound hamburger
diced shallots or green onions
1/3 cup taco sauce
1/2 head lettuce, sliced finely
grated mild cheddar cheese
2 fresh tomatoes, diced
1/2 pint sour cream

Saute hamburger and onions slowly then mix well with taco sauce. On a serving plate, layer 1/4 hamburger mixture, then lettuce, cheese, and tomatoes and a generous dollop of sour cream on top. Serves 4.

Jessica Oliver – Honolulu, Hawaii

salad vintner

2 heads Bibb lettuce
1/2 head romaine
1 bunch watercress
1/2 cup walnut halves
    or chopped walnuts
1/2 cup grated gruyere cheese
1/2 cup olive oil
2 tablespoons red wine
1 tablespoon + 1 teaspoon
    red wine vinegar
1 tablespoon Dijon mustard
1 teaspoon salt
3/4 teaspoon freshly ground pepper

Wash greens, dry thoroughly and chill. Combine with walnuts and gruyere in large salad bowl. Thoroughly blend remaining ingredients in small bowl or jar with tight fitting lid. Just before serving, pour over salad and toss gently.

Marylou Brogan – Honolulu, Hawaii

bay shrimp salad

2 pounds bay shrimp, cooked
1 cup fresh mint leaves, chopped
1 cup fresh parsley, chopped
3 cups tomatoes, diced
1-1/2 cups cucumber, diced
1 cup red onion, minced
1 cup mayonnaise
4 tablespoons lemon juice
6 tablespoons olive oil
1 teaspoon salt
1/4 teaspoon white pepper
24 red or leaf lettuce leaves

Press shrimp lightly between palms of hands to remove excess moisture, then refrigerate. Rinse lettuce leaves, spin or pat dry and refrigerate. Peel cucumber and remove seeds from cucumber and tomatoes before dicing.

Combine shrimp, tomatoes, cucumber, onion, mint and parsley, then refrigerate. Combine mayonnaise, lemon juice, olive oil, salt and white pepper and refrigerate. When ready to serve, pour over salad and toss lightly.

…for your presentation, place 2 lettuce leaves in opposite directions on salad plates. Heap individual servings of salad on lettuce. Serves 12.

Ken Stehouwer – Honolulu, Hawaii

caesar salad

1 large (preferably unfinished wood)
    bowl
1 garlic bud
1/2 teaspoon salt
1/4 teaspoon freshly ground pepper
4 to 6 anchovy fillets
1 to 1-1/2 tablespoons vinegar
3 tablespoons salad oil
1/2 teaspoon Coleman's dry mustard
1 teaspoon Worcestershire sauce
juice from 1/2 fresh lemon
3 large handfuls romaine lettuce
1 coddled egg
approximately 3 heaping tablespoons
    grated Parmesan cheese
1 cup crisp toasted croutons

Rub garlic bud around the bowl thoroughly, mash until thoroughly mashed up.
Add salt and pepper, then anchovy. Again mash around the bowl until you
have a smooth paste. Add vinegar, salad oil, dry mustard, Worcestershire sauce
and lemon juice. Mix everything thoroughly. Shake lettuce in a large cloth to
remove moisture. Add lettuce to bowl and toss well. Break egg over lettuce and toss
again. Sprinkle Parmesan cheese and croutons over salad and toss again.
Serve immediately. Serves 2.

Jacque Orenstein – Oklahoma City, Oklahoma
Creative Cookery and Jacques

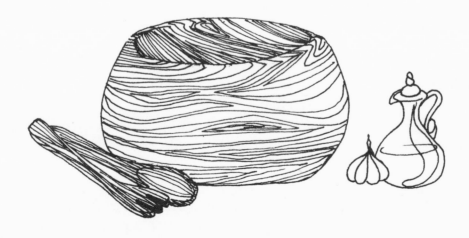

mustard

mustard

Mediterranean origin...in ancient days, the Romans created a confection by pounding its seed with new wine, cinnamon and enough honey to form the mixture into small balls...in India, mustard is the symbol of rebirth or re-incarnation... the pungency of mustard is achieved by an enzyme action requiring liquid, hence powdered mustard is devoid of these qualities normally associated with this herb.

Accompaniments, Salad Dressings, Sauces

curried fruit

1/2 cup melted butter
2 tablespoons curry powder
1-1/2 cups brown sugar
3 large cans or jars of Libby's fruit salad
3 cans pineapple chunks

Drain off a little more than half of the liquid from the fruit. Mix butter, sugar and curry together, stirring together over heat. Remove from heat and toss fruit with curry mixture. Put into a large casserole and bake 30 minutes at 325°. Serves 30.

Eva Pocklington – Edmonton, Alberta, Canada

baked papaya

4 papayas (small or medium)
1-1/2 to 2 cups brown sugar
juice of 2 lemons
1 stick butter

Skin papayas and remove seeds. Cut into quarters and into halves again. Place in a deep pan. Sprinkle with sugar and lemon juice and dot with butter. Bake at 350° for about 30 minutes.

Sugar and Spice

papaya poi—tahitian style

4 papayas, mashed
2 tablespoons brown sugar
1 cup corn starch
1 vanilla bean
1/2 cup coconut milk
1/4 pineapple, mashed

Simmer mashed papaya with brown sugar and pineapple until mushy, then cool. Add starch and vanilla bean. Add a little water and bake at 350° to 400° for 1 hour or until very brown on top. When ready to serve, pour coconut milk mixed with brown sugar on top…super delicious!

Carla Beachcomber – Honolulu, Hawaii

piccalilli

1 gallon green tomatoes
1 quart cabbage
1 quart onions
10 green peppers
2 tablespoons celery seed
2 tablespoons mustard seed

1 quart sweet pickles, diced
2 cups celery, ground and cut up
1 can green beans, cut up
1/4 cup corn starch
3 pints vinegar
4 or 5 cups sugar

Grind first four ingredients and add a handful of salt. Let set overnight.

In the morning, drain. In a large pot on stove, add 3 pints of vinegar and sugar, (4-5 or more cups) to make a sweet-sour liquid, add celery seed and mustard seed. Bring to a boil and add sweet pickles, ground celery and green beans. Cook 15-20 minutes and stir often. When done add corn starch for thickening and some green food coloring for looks. Ready to can and makes about 7 plus quarts.

Dorothy P. Crawford – Ponca City, Oklahoma

mango chutney

6 quarts cider vinegar
16 pounds ripe mangoes
1/2 pound onion
2 teaspoons each: minced garlic, celery seed, chili pepper (or 1 hot chili pepper)
1 tablespoon each: ground nutmeg, cinnamon, allspice
1/2 pound citron peel
1-1/2 pounds seedless raisins
10 pounds brown sugar
1/2 pound preserved ginger in syrup
1/2 pound currants
1/2 pound blanched almonds

Peel and slice mangoes. Finely chop ginger and onions. Chop pepper (wear gloves). Chop citron peel. Boil vinegar and sugar. Add mangoes, 1/4 at a time so mixture keeps boiling. Boil 10 minutes. Add ginger, onion and garlic. Boil 1 hour more and add remaining ingredients. Boil 1 hour more over low heat. Pour, boiling, into hot, sterilized jars.

Yield: 33 6-ounce jars

Barbara Bell – Aspen, Colorado

mango and papaya butter sauce

6 ounces mango pulp
24 ounces papaya puree (peeled and
    seeds removed)
8 ounces butter
1-1/2 ounces lime juice
1 quart water
2 ounces red currant jelly
1/2 cup sugar
1/4 ounce white vinegar
1 ounce Madeira wine
1 ounce brandy
1/2 ounce orange juice
2 ounces corn starch dissolved with
    4 ounces water

Grind or puree the papaya. In a heavy skillet, caramelize the sugar with the vinegar. Add the papaya puree and all other ingredients except Madeira wine and brandy. Simmer for 20 minutes. Bind with corn starch to your preferred thickness. Add Madeira and brandy. Simmer for one minute, then strain.

A good sauce to serve with sauteed mahi mahi.

George Mendreshora – Honolulu, Hawaii
Executive Chef, United Airlines

fruit salad dressing

10 tablespoons sugar
1 teaspoon salt
1 teaspoon dry mustard
1 large grated onion
1 cup salad oil
1/2 cup vinegar
4 tablespoons celery seed

Beat sugar, salt, mustard and onion with salad oil in a blender, adding vinegar very, very slowly. Add celery seed last.

…this is great on all fruit salads.

Maxine Van Winkle Treat – Santa Cruz, California

ginger sesame dressing

1 tablespoon fresh ginger
10 ounces heavy mayonnaise
1/2 cup salad oil
1-1/2 ounces cider vinegar
4 drops Tabasco sauce
4 drops Worcestershire sauce
2 ounces white wine
1 tablespoon toasted sesame seeds
1 teaspoon lemon juice
1 pinch garlic salt
2 pinches salt
1 pinch ground black pepper

Peel and chop the ginger. In a mixing bowl, blend the mayonnaise, oil and vinegar. Then add the remaining ingredients. Whip gently for one minute and refrigerate for one hour before serving.

George Mendreshora – Honolulu, Hawaii

french dressing

1/3 cup granulated sugar
1 teaspoon salt
dash of black pepper and paprika
2/3 cup salad oil
1/3 cup red wine vinegar

Mix ingredients as listed. Shake vigorously. Shake each time before using…I save empty vinegar bottles and use a funnel. However this could be mixed in a bowl, with a beater, or in a blender. In that case you may want to add the oil and vinegar first. Garlic flavored vinegar may be used.

Mabel Chapson – Honolulu, Hawaii

hank's favorite dressing

1 quart mayonnaise
1 pound bleu cheese, grated
dash of Worcestershire sauce

Mix all ingredients in a bowl. Store in glass jars in the refrigerator. You can use the same mayonnaise jar. This can be used for salad dressing, as a dip with chips, and it is wonderful on ham sandwiches.

Alzada Black – Ponca City, Oklahoma

bearnaise sauce

4 egg yolks
1 cup butter
1 tablespoon lemon juice
1 tablespoon tarragon vinegar
1/4 teaspoon salt (optional)
1 teaspoon chopped parsley
1 teaspoon onion juice
dash of cayenne pepper

Place egg yolks with one third of the butter in the top of a double boiler. Keep water in the bottom of boiler hot but not boiling. Add remaining butter as sauce thickens, stirring constantly. Remove from heat and add remaining ingredients. Serve with broiled beef tenderloin.

Evelyn Nordquist – Honolulu, Hawaii

hollandaise sauce

5 egg yolks
1 tablespoon lemon juice
1 teaspoon salt
dash cayenne
1 cup butter

This can be made in a food processor or blender. If using the processor, use the steel blade. Place egg yolks, lemon juice, salt and cayenne in the container, switch on, then immediately off. Heat butter to a boil. With motor running, pour hot butter into the container in a steady stream. Turn off immediately. Keep the sauce warm over hot water but not boiling water. Makes 2 cups.

Betty and Baker Horner – Tulsa, Oklahoma

fresh tomato sauce for pasta

2-1/2 pounds red, ripe tomatoes,
    chopped
4 large cloves garlic, peeled and left whole
1 small hot red or green chili, chopped
1/2 cup coarsely chopped fresh basil
salt and pepper to taste
1/2 cup parsley
1/2 cup olive oil
1 pound penne or similar tubular pasta
1/2 pound fontina or muenster,
    coarsely grated
1/2 cup grated Parmesan

Combine all ingredients except pasta and cheeses. Let stand at room temperature for several hours, or refrigerate overnight and return to room temperature.

Cook pasta and drain. Spoon off 1/4 cup of the surface oil from tomato mixture and add to pasta. Add Parmesan cheese and toss. Add 1/2 of tomato sauce. Crumble fontina into 1/2 of remaining sauce, add to pasta and toss. Serve in bowls with remaining sauce spooned on top.

…for this recipe, you must use ripe tomatoes, i.e., tasting tomatoes, not the hothouse, tasteless variety.

Glenda Pell – Honolulu, Hawaii

marinara sauce

4 tablespoons olive oil
2 cups finely chopped onions
4 cloves garlic, minced
3 28-ounce cans Italian plum tomatoes
2 7-ounce cans tomato paste
1 tablespoon dried basil
2 tablespoons sugar
1 tablespoon salt
freshly ground pepper

Heat olive oil in large pan, add onions and garlic. Cook over moderate heat for 6-7 minutes or until just soft and not browned. Put canned tomatoes in blender (one can at a time) and blend for 3-4 seconds only. Add to onion mixture. Add rest of ingredients. Cook till bubbling. Reduce heat to low and simmer with pan partially covered for about 30 minutes. Stir occasionally.

Marjorie Wilson – Honolulu, Hawaii

93

hill's hawaiian ham sauce

1 cup hot pepper jelly*
1/4 cup butter
juice of 1/2 fresh lemon
1 cup pineapple cubes
1/2 cup cherries
1/4 cup cream sherry

Melt butter and add lemon juice. Blend in hot pepper jelly, add pineapple and cherries. Simmer 10 minutes, stirring occasionally. Remove from heat and add sherry. Serve over thickly sliced baked ham.

*I use Judyth's Mountain Hot Pepper Jelly.

David Hill – Honolulu Hawaii

mustard sauce

3 tablespoons dry mustard
2 teaspoons sugar
3/4 teaspoon salt
2 tablespoons water
2 tablespoons white vinegar
dash of red pepper
1 tablespoon butter
whipping cream

Cook in a double boiler until thick. Remove from stove and add butter. When serving, add a little cream.

Misayo Kikuchi – Honolulu, Hawaii

remoulade sauce

In a food processor place:
    1 jar capers – drained
    8 ounces drained sweet gherkins

Chop finely then remove to mixing bowl and add:
    10 to 12 tablespoons mayonnaise
    1 teaspoon mustard
    1 teaspoon curry powder
    1/4 teaspoon salt
    dash of white pepper

Mix well, and use cold on cold cut meats as a sandwich spread, or as one of the sauces for meat fondue.

Jorgen Skov – Honolulu, Hawaii

94

garlic and parsley sauce

5 cloves garlic minced very fine
5 tablespoons parsley chopped very fine
juice of 1 lemon
1 teaspoon Vege-Salt

Mix all ingredients and serve.

Lilia Lee – Honolulu, Hawaii

sauce for fish

1 cup heavy cream or crème fraiche
2 egg yolks slightly beaten
1/2 teaspoon shallots – minced
1/4 teaspoon lemon peel – grated
1/4 teaspoon each parsley, chervil and
      tarragon – chopped
1/2 teaspoon Dijon mustard
beurre manie (1 teaspoon butter mixed
      with 1 teaspoon flour)
juice of 1 lemon

Mix cream and yolks together and add seasonings and mustard. Heat over low fire, stirring constantly. As sauce thickens, stir in beurre manie and cook until sauce is thick, being careful not to boil. It can be held over warm water. Just before serving, stir in lemon juice.

Nancy Kennedy – Honolulu, Hawaii

spaghetti sauce for sugar and spice

1 cup chopped onion
1 pound ground beef
3 cloves garlic, minced
1 bell pepper, chopped
1 1-pound-14-ounce can tomatoes,
    cut up
1 10-ounce can tomato soup
1 6-ounce can tomato paste
1/4 cup snipped parsley or dried parsley
1 tablespoon brown sugar
1 teaspoon salt
1-1/2 teaspoons oregano
1/4 teaspoon thyme
1 bay leaf
1 8-ounce can mushrooms

Cook onion and beef until browned. Drain and transfer to a large pot. Add
the remaining ingredients and simmer for 3 hours. When simmered, serve over
thin vermicelli noodles. Serves 6. Serve grated Parmesan cheese on top.

…when boiling the spaghetti add 2 tablespoons cooking oil. This keeps the
spaghetti from sticking.

Janee Dimmitt and Vicky Strickland – Honolulu, Hawaii
Florence Wallace – Ponca City, Oklahoma

dill and lemon mayonnaise

2 whole eggs
2 teaspoons Dijon mustard
1/4 lemon – juice only
1/2 teaspoon salt
1-1/2 cups salad oil
1 teaspoon dill weed or 1 tablespoon fresh dill

In a blender or food processor, add the eggs, mustard, lemon juice and salt. Whirl for a few moments, then slowly add the salad oil. Do not chill or it will be too thick for covering the fish.

Lavonne Tollerud – Honolulu, Hawaii

mustard sauce

In a blender or food processor, mix 1/4 cup Dijon mustard and 1/4 cup mayonnaise. Add a dash of dill weed before serving.

Lilia Lee – Honolulu, Hawaii

chili sauce

1/4 cup chili sauce, or Del Monte
    cocktail sauce
1 tablespoon Tabasco sauce
1 tablespoon Worcestershire sauce
1 tablespoon A-1 sauce

Stir sauces together and serve.

Lilia Lee – Honolulu, Hawaii

ambrosia pecan sauce

1 cup granulated sugar
1 cup boiling water
pinch of salt
1/2 cup coarsely chopped pecans, toasted
1 cup marshmallow cream, 9 ounces
    as purchased
1 teaspoon vanilla

Spread layer of sugar over bottom of iron skillet. Stir gently and continuously over low heat until sugar is liquified and is dark amber in color. This will take about 30 minutes. Remove skillet from heat. Gradually add boiling water and salt. Return to heat. Stir and cook, simmering for 10 minutes. Pour into nonmetallic bowls. Add vanilla and nuts. Allow to cool. Stir in marshmallow cream.

Patricia Kelley Hemmeter – Honolulu, Hawaii

hot fudge topping

1/2 pound butter
4 squares unsweetened chocolate
4 cups powdered sugar
1 large can condensed milk

In a heavy pan, melt the butter and chocolate over low heat. Add the powdered sugar and stir until the mixture is smooth. Add the milk and allow the mixture to simmer for about 10 minutes. Serve hot over ice cream.

…this recipe is very thick when cold, so if you plan to eat it cold, add more milk.

…always heat in a double boiler when you are reheating the fudge.

Lavonne Tollerud – Honolulu, Hawaii

chocolate sauce

2 cups canned milk
3 cups sugar
1 bar Baker's Bitter Chocolate
1/4 cup butter

Combine all ingredients. Cook in a double boiler for 7 minutes. Add 1 teaspoon vanilla.

…this sauce keeps very well if you <u>hide</u> it!

Jessie Brown – Honolulu, Hawaii

mango sauce for ice cream

32 ounces canned mangoes
1/4 cup white Bacardi rum
3/4 cup sugar
1/2 ounce fresh lemon juice
3/4 cup heavy cream for whipping
1/4 cup chopped macadamia nuts

Strain the juice from the mangoes and dice them. Place the syrup in a heavy skillet and add the rum, sugar and lemon juice. Simmer for 10 minutes then add the diced mangoes. Bring to a boil. Cool. Top vanilla ice cream with mango sauce. Decorate with whipped cream and sprinkle with macadamia nuts.

George Mendreshora – Honolulu, Hawaii

raspberry quick sauce

1 10-ounce package frozen raspberries
      in syrup or sweetened with sugar
juice of 1 lemon

Combine the raspberries in a food processor fitted with a metal chopping blade and process until a smooth sauce forms…you can strain seeds for an unnecessary bit of elegance. Serve with poached fruit, fresh fruit, ice cream, cake or anything else you like…

By the way, anything you use this sauce on becomes ' à la cardinal'.

Carl Jerome – Aspen, Colorado

rhubarb sauce

1-1/2 pounds fresh rhubarb stems
1/2 cup water
1/8 teaspoon salt
1/2 to 2/3 cup sugar

Wash rhubarb, cut off root and leaf ends. Cut into 1- or 2-inch pieces without peeling. Combine all ingredients in a saucepan. Simmer, covered, until tender, usually between 10 and 20 minutes, stirring gently a few times. Refrigerate.

Betty and Art Pfister – Aspen, Colorado

chive

chive

Mediterranean origin...used in ancient days as a remedy for bleeding, it was also a favorite plant in the royal herb gardens of Europe during the middle ages...while a member of the lily family, chives impart a delicate onion taste and smell to food.

Eggs & Cheese

scotch eggs

6 - 8 hard boiled eggs
2 - 3 eggs, raw
flour for dusting
1 pound sausage
fine bread crumbs

Preheat oven to 400°. Dip boiled eggs into beaten eggs, then roll in flour. Press the sausage around the eggs, and again dip into the beaten eggs, then in the fine bread crumbs. Deep-fat fry the coated eggs in oil heated to 375°. Fry for 3 to 4 minutes until the crumbs are golden brown. Place the fried and drained eggs in the preheated oven for 10 minutes. Serve cold.

Lavonne Tollerud – Honolulu, Hawaii
Creative Cookery

eggs alexandra

12 hard boiled eggs
1 stick butter
3 shallots
1 cup ground fresh mushrooms
1 cup ground ham
6 cups medium white sauce
1 cup bread crumbs
salt and pepper

Halve eggs lengthwise. Scoop out yolks and grind fine in a food processor or push through a fine sieve. Saute shallots and mushrooms about 5 minutes in 4 tablespoons butter. Season with salt and pepper to taste. Combine mushroom mixture with ham and yolks and 1 cup white sauce. Fill egg whites with the mixture, shaping like a full egg and sprinkle with bread crumbs. Butter a flat baking dish, pour some of the white sauce in, and arrange the eggs in it. Pour remaining sauce over them. Sprinkle with bread crumbs, dot with butter, and bake at 375° until hot and golden. Serves 6.

Tita Kaspar – Aspen, Colorado

brunch casserole

1/2 pound dried beef, cut up
4 slices bacon, fried and crumbled
1/2 cup butter
2 cups mushroom soup
1 soup can of milk
16 slightly beaten eggs
1/4 teaspoon salt
2/3 cup evaporated milk
1 cup cheddar cheese, grated
6 to 8 sliced mushrooms

Heat dried beef and crumbled bacon until hot in 1/4 cup butter. Mix mushroom soup with milk until smooth. Heat thoroughly. Add to beef mixture. Scramble eggs in remaining butter. Add salt and evaporated milk. Scramble eggs until cooked and very moist. Layer with beef mixture and cheese in a 9 x 13 x 2-inch casserole, arrange mushrooms on top. Place in 250° oven to keep warm until serving time. Casserole will keep well for 1 hour in oven. Serves 10.

Sugar and Spice

cheese souffle roll

7 eggs, separated
1/3 cup butter
6 tablespoons flour
dash cayenne
3/4 teaspoon salt
1-1/4 cups milk
1/2 cup grated Parmesan cheese
1/2 cup grated cheddar cheese
1/4 teaspoon cream of tartar

spinach filling

2 10-ounce packages frozen
    spinach (chopped)
2 tablespoons butter
1/4 cup grated onion
1/4 teaspoon salt
1/4 cup grated cheddar cheese
1/2 cup sour cream
6 cheese slices, cut diagonally

Separate the eggs, bring to room temperature. Grease a jelly-roll pan, line with wax paper, grease paper. Melt butter, stir in flour, cayenne, 1/2 teaspoon salt. Take off heat and stir in milk. Cook, stirring until mixture is thick and leaves bottom of pan. Beat in Parmesan and cheddar cheeses. Beat egg whites in a mixer with 1/4 teaspoon salt and cream of tartar until stiff peaks form. Fold 1/3 of whites into cheese mixture. Carefully fold in remaining whites, turn into pan. Bake 15 minutes at 350° Meanwhile, "back at the ranch"…make filling.

Turn spinach into a sieve and press out water. Saute onion in butter until golden. Add spinach, salt, cheddar cheese, and sour cream. Mix well. Invert souffle on wax paper (double thickness) sprinkled with Parmesan cheese. Peel off wax paper, spread with spinach filling. Roll up from long side. Place seam side down on greased cookie sheet. Arrange cheese slices over top and broil about 4 minutes until cheese melts. May be frozen.

Judy Richardson – Kailua, Hawaii

cauliflower souffle

1/2 cup flour
1/2 cup butter
1-1/4 cups warm milk
5 eggs, separated
1 teaspoon sugar
salt and white pepper to taste
1 head cauliflower broken into
     small flowerettes

Make a roux from the flour, butter and milk, cool and add egg yolks. Then add salt, pepper and sugar to taste. Finally, fold in stiffly beaten egg whites. Coat an ovenproof souffle dish inside with butter and then pat with a layer of bread crumbs. If done in advance, keep cool in the refrigerator.

Fill the dish 3/4 full with alternating layers of mixture and cauliflower, making sure the final layer of cauliflower is covered.

Preheat oven to 400° Place dish in middle of oven, and immediately reduce heat to 375° Souffle should be done in approximately 45 minutes, but is wise to keep an eye on the progress. It will rise about 1 inch above the edge of the dish.

Remove when brown and serve immediately pouring melted butter over each serving.

…this can be made in individual small dishes, then be aware of shorter cooking time.

                                        Jorgen Skov – Honolulu, Hawaii

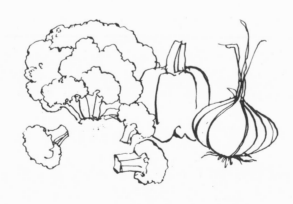

broccoli souffle

1 10-ounce package frozen chopped
    broccoli
1 12 or 16-ounce carton cottage cheese
3 eggs
1 teaspoon garlic salt
dash of pepper
1/4 teaspoon lemon juice
2 6-ounce packages muenster
    cheese, sliced
6 ounces sharp cheddar

Thaw the broccoli, and mix with cottage cheese, beaten eggs, garlic salt, pepper, lemon juice, and shredded cheddar cheese.

Line an 8 x 8-inch or 1-1/2 quart container with one package of muenster cheese. Add mixed ingredients, and cover with another package of muenster cheese. Cover and bake at 350° for 45 minutes. Serves 8 to 10.

Mitzi B. Wade – Marietta, Georgia

crabmeat quiche

2 6-ounce cans white crabmeat
1/2 onion, chopped
2 tablespoons parsley, chopped
1/2 cup celery, chopped
1 green pepper, chopped
2 pastry shells, uncooked
1 cup grated cheddar cheese

1/3 cup grated Parmesan cheese
6 eggs, beaten
1/4 cup flour
2-1/2 cups whipping cream
cayenne and seasoned salt to taste
1 teaspoon Worcestershire sauce
2 tablespoons fresh lemon juice

Combine crabmeat, onion, celery, green pepper, and parsley and divide equally between the two pastry shells. Sprinkle each with 1/2 of the cheddar and 1/2 of the Parmesan cheeses. Combine the rest of the ingredients in a bowl and mix well. Pour 1/2 of this mixture into each quiche. Bake in 350° oven for 40-45 minutes or until set. Serve individual slices topped with hollandaise sauce. The sauce is most important.

Betty Horner – Tulsa, Oklahoma

kielbasa quiche

crust

3/4 cup raw wheat germ
1/2 cup unbleached white flour
1/4 cup unsalted butter
1 egg

filling

3 eggs
2 cups half and half
1/4 teaspoon thyme
1/4 teaspoon dill weed
pepper to taste
1 cup grated Swiss cheese
1 cup grated mild cheddar
1 pound kielbasa (Polish sausage)
2 large mushroom caps
    sliced evenly
1/2 cup chopped fresh chives

To make the crust, combine wheat germ and flour in a bowl. Cut in butter with a pastry blender until it resembles coarse meal. Add egg and blend well. Press mixture into the bottom and sides of a lightly buttered fluted quiche pan. Bake at 425° for 10 minutes. Cool on rack.

Reduce oven temperature to 350°. Prepare filling while pastry cools. Combine all ingredients except sausage, cheese and mushrooms in a large bowl. Slice sausage into 1/4 inch rounds then cut each round in half. Add sausage and cheese by lightly stirring into egg mixture. Pour into baked pastry. Stir carefully to distribute cheese. Place only flat slices of mushroom caps end to end to form a circle in center top of filling.

Bake at 350° for 30-35 minutes or until silver knife inserted in center comes out clean. Cool on rack 5 minutes before serving. Serves 6.

Pat Wozniak – Honolulu, Hawaii

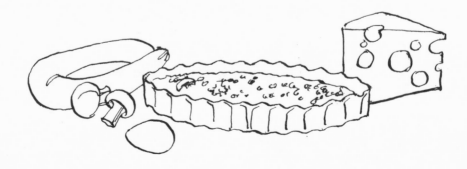

canneloni ranieri

1 quart small curd cottage cheese
5 eggs
2 packages chopped frozen spinach
1/2 teaspoon salt
pepper to taste
1/4 to 1/2 teaspoon nutmeg

20 crepes
20 slices Monterey Jack cheese
Parmesan cheese, grated

It is important to cook spinach just until thawed and hot. Drain spinach well. Spinach must be very dry so as not to make cheese mixture too soupy. Take small amounts of spinach and squeeze all water out with hands. Chop spinach fine.

In a large bowl, combine cottage cheese, eggs, salt and pepper, nutmeg and spinach. Mix well. Have ready approximately 2-1/2 quarts of your favorite marinara sauce.* Spread a small amount of sauce on the bottom of 2 large pyrex baking dishes 13-1/2 x 8-3/4 x 1-3/4 inches. Put 2 heaping tablespoons of filling in the center of each crepe. Roll crepe and place seam-side down in baking dish.

Arrange 10 filled crepes in each dish. Spoon some sauce over and around crepes. Reserve 1/2 of the sauce. Bake at 350° for approximately 55 minutes or until they start to puff up. Top each crepe with a thin slice of Jack cheese, and cook 5 minutes longer. Serves 10.

Serve with extra sauce around crepes. Top with freshly grated Parmesan cheese.

crepes for canneloni

8 eggs
2 cups flour
3 cups milk
1/2 teaspoon salt
5 tablespoons melted butter

Beat eggs until light. Add flour and mix well. Slowly add milk, mixing constantly so mixture won't be lumpy. Add salt and melted butter. Mix. Heat a 10 inch fry pan over medium heat. Put 1-2 teaspoons butter in pan and heat until sizzling. Pour in 1/4 cup batter and tip pan so it will spread out in a thin layer. Cook until dry on top and lightly flecked with brown on bottom.

Do not turn crepes over. Remove from pan and repeat process, adding butter each time. Makes 20.

Marjorie Wilson – Honolulu, Hawaii

*See Sauces

chili rellenos

Open and drain, canned whole green chili peppers, 1/2 per person.

Stuff peppers with sliced Monterey Jack cheese.

Make a batter: use 1 egg for each 2 peppers. Separate whites and beat to a stiff consistency. Season with salt, pepper, and oregano. Add the yolks and beat lightly until smooth. You may add 1 teaspoon flour for each 2 eggs to thicken.

Preheat large frying pan to 400° with a thin layer of oil. Dip the stuffed peppers in the batter and fry in oil. Turn when lightly browned.

Serve while hot with appropriate hot salsa.

Dr. Jim Penoff – Honolulu, Hawaii

jam's chalupas

1 pound dried pinto beans
1 ham hock
1 teaspoon salt
1 pound shredded cheddar
    (sharp)
1/2 head lettuce
2 tomatoes
2 avocados
1 onion

Cook beans in a large pot and add ham and salt and water to cover 1/2 inch above. Simmer until all water is absorbed and beans are cooked (mushy). Dice and chop lettuce, tomatoes, avocados and onion.

Have sour cream, hot sauce, crushed fritos, on each plate. Put chips, then layer warm beans, cheese, etc. Top with sour cream and hot sauce.

Jam Majors – Dallas, Texas

jack lord's aloha eggs

1/2 cup celery
2 tablespoons green pepper
2 tablespoons ham
1/2 cup tofu (bean curd)
3 large eggs
1 tablespoon soy sauce
2 squirts Tabasco sauce
1 tablespoon clarified butter

Start heating a 10-inch teflon coated pan on the lowest flame while preparing ingredients. Saute in an 8-inch frying pan until just cooked, not too soft, the chopped celery, chopped green pepper and chopped onion. Add chopped ham and 1/2 inch cubed tofu to sauteed vegetables, just to heat through. Beat eggs slightly, adding soy sauce and tabasco. Increase heat under large pan to high, and pour in clarified butter.

Add beaten eggs, swirl around with a wooden spoon. Add mixture from smaller pan and gently mix for scrambled eggs. Serve with soy sauce if desired.

Jack Lord likes eggs with tofu, and soy sauce. Marie says it could be served at breakfast or luncheon.

Marie Lord – Honolulu, Hawaii

blintz casserole

1-1/2 cups cottage cheese
1 teaspoon grated lemon rind
2 teaspoons vanilla
4 eggs
1-1/2 cups sour cream
1/4 teaspoon salt
1/4 cup sugar
4 tablespoons melted butter
1/4 cup orange juice
12 crepes

Mix cottage cheese, lemon rind, 1 egg yolk and 1 teaspoon vanilla. Fill crepes with cottage cheese mixture and roll into 12 blintzes. Lightly brush blintzes with butter and place in a 9 x 13-inch dish. Beat remaining eggs. Add sour cream, 1 teaspoon vanilla, salt, sugar, and orange juice, and beat again. Pour over blintzes and refrigerate before baking. Bake at 350° for 45 minutes or until set.

Linda Soll – Honolulu, Hawaii

thyme

thyme

Mediterranean origin...this unassuming
plant appears from the ground in thick, pink
to semi-violet cushions and seems to grow
right out of the naked native rock and
have no need for water...it is true,
this member of the mint family lives
almost entirely on cosmic sources, on sun
and warmth.

Seafood

mullet in ti leaves

Clean fresh mullet and sprinkle with Hawaiian salt lightly. Place on 6 or 8 ti leaves. Add several tablespoons coconut cream and fold leaves around fish to make a compact bundle. Bake at 400° for 20-30 minutes. If coconut cream isn't used, put a lump of butter under fish.

...in Honolulu, Mendonca's coconut cream or coconut milk is found in the frozen canned section of the market.

...fresh cleaned mullet is available at super markets or fish markets.

...rock salt can be used for Hawaiian salt.

Lucy Blaisdell – Honolulu, Hawaii

salmon souffle

1 15-1/2-ounce can salmon
1 4-ounce can mushrooms and liquid
1/2 cup green pepper, cut small
1 cup milk
1 can mushroom soup
1 8-ounce package shredded cheddar
      cheese
1 grated onion
1/2 cup bread crumbs
3 eggs, well beaten

Mix together well and bake at 350° for 1 hour.

Dale Solheim – Aspen, Colorado

trout souffle

10 trout fillets
1 pound fillet of snapper
2/3 quart fresh cream
5 egg whites
8 ounces butter
1 ounce chopped shallots
1/2 ounce dry white wine
1 teaspoon lemon juice
salt and pepper

Fillet five medium size trouts. Take fillet of snapper and pound with a pestle in a very hard bowl (mortar). When you have a paste-like substance, add a little salt and pepper, half of the fresh cream and the whipped egg whites. Evenly cover the trout fillets with this mixture. Place in a buttered pan with shallots and the white wine. Bake in oven uncovered for 15 minutes at 380° Remove fillets.

Sauce: Add remaining cream, lemon juice to the liquid you gain from the fillet. Reduce by half and serve on a warm plate. Ladle sauce beneath fish. Garnish with watercress.

Serve with a light Riesling wine.

Serves 10 as an appetizer, 5 as a main course.

Fred Hellekes – Liberty House
Honolulu, Hawaii

poached salmon or red snapper

4 cups chicken stock
1 cup dry white wine
celery tops
1 onion, sliced
1 carrot, sliced
4 sprigs of parsley
1 bay leaf
1 teaspoon thyme
2 tablespoons salt
10 peppercorns
salmon or red snapper (whole)

Simmer all above ingredients for 20 minutes before poaching fish.

Wrap fish in cheese cloth for easier handling and lower into the poaching liquid. Poach for 10 minutes per inch (measure at the thickest part of the fish's body). When cooked, remove and place on a platter. When slightly cooled, remove skin from the sides of the fish. Cover the fish and chill until ready to coat with mayonnaise (see sauces). Slice about six lemons or limes in very thin slices for decoration.

Lavonne Tollerud – Honolulu, Hawaii

fillet of mahi mahi plantation

30 ounces fillet of mahi mahi (fresh)
1/2 ounce soy sauce
2 ounces all purpose flour
2 ounces oil
2 whole eggs, beaten
2 ounces butter
1/2 teaspoon fresh chives (chopped)

1/2 ounce lemon juice
6 lemon wedges
6 pieces red pimento
1/2 ounce toasted coconut chips
1 ounce salted peanut halves
6 parsley sprigs
salt and pepper to taste

Divide the fillets of mahi mahi into 5-ounce portions. Season with salt and pepper. Marinate with soy sauce and lemon juice for 30 minutes, then dip the fillets in flour and beaten eggs. Saute in a heavy skillet in hot oil until golden brown on both sides, then bake in a 350° oven for 15 minutes. Saute peanuts and chives in hot butter for 1 minute. Place the mahi mahi on a serving dish. Top with the butter, chives and peanuts, then sprinkle with the toasted coconut. Decorate with red pimento cut into 1-1/2 inch strips, sprigs of parsley and lemon. Serves 6.

George Mendreshora – Honolulu, Hawaii

poached salmon and egg sauce

1 4 to 5-pound salmon
2 cups water
2 stalks celery
1/2 lemon, sliced
1/2 onion, sliced
1 bay leaf
egg sauce (recipe follows)

Wrap salmon in cheesecloth and place in a large, shallow pan. Add water, celery, lemon, onion and bay leaf. Cover pan with foil and simmer until fish flakes easily when poked with a fork, about 25 to 30 minutes. Carefully unwrap fish and remove skin without breaking fish apart. Reserve 1 cup of fish stock. Transfer fish to warm serving platter and top with egg sauce. Makes 8 to 10 servings.

egg sauce

In a medium pan melt 1/4 cup butter, blend in 3 tablespoons flour, 1/2 teaspoon salt and 1/4 teaspoon white pepper. Add fish stock and 1 cup light cream. Stir over low heat until thickened. Add 2 chopped hard boiled eggs and heat through. Decorate with parsley or other greens. Pour over fish.

Michael Eith – Honolulu, Hawaii

lau—lau

1 bunch taro leaves (ask your
    produce man for it)
2 pounds stewing pork
3/4 pound butterfish
3/4 pound salted salmon
ti leaves

Wash taro leaves and remove all the stem parts from the back of each leaf. Put a piece of pork between a smaller piece of butterfish and salted salmon. Wrap well in about 6 small taro leaves, or 3 large ones. Roll up tightly in the leaves and tie. Put into a steamer and steam for 3 to 4 hours. Serves 8.

Lucy Blaisdell – Honolulu, Hawaii

charcoal broiled salmon tail

The tail cut of salmon is preferable to salmon steaks. Not only do you not have to be concerned with bones, but the texture of the flesh is superior. When you buy the tail section, make sure it is taken off the bone, but the skin is left on.

When the coals are ready for cooking, lightly coat the grill with cooking oil. Also lightly oil the salmon skin and place the fish skin-side down, on the grill.

Salt, pepper, and fresh lemon juice are the only seasonings necessary. Fifteen minutes is about right, with the skin-side down for the first 10. Turn the fish, skin and all, for the final 5 minutes.

Under-do it. It can always go back for a minute or two, but if over done, it is very dry.

Steamed, fresh peas, and boiled new potatoes are a nice complement.

…it's tough to beat a good Chardonnay with this meal.

Stephen R. Arelt – Mill Valley, California

fresh cold lobster

(bouche amoureuse)

Tie together in a bag of cheesecloth:
- 1/4 cup chopped leeks
- 1/4 cup chopped onion
- 1/4 cup chopped carrot
- 1/4 cup chopped celery
- 1 bay leaf
- 1 tablespoon freshly crushed
    black peppercorns
- 1 sprig thyme
- 4 threads saffron
- 1-1/2 teaspoons Hawaiian rock salt

- 4 cups dry white wine
- 4 cups water
- 1 fresh lobster about 1-1/2 pounds,
    or 2 small ones
- 1/2 head lettuce, shredded
- 1 lemon, thinly sliced
- 2 slices smoked Canadian salmon
- 2 slices toast (4 triangles)
- 2 tablespoons Beluga caviar
- 2 hard boiled eggs, sliced
- 1/4 cup capers
- 1 tablespoon buttered bread crumbs

Bring the white wine and water to boil with the bag of vegetables, then put the lobster in and make sure it is fully submerged. Boil for fifteen minutes and leave it in cooking liquid to cool. Cut the lobster in half and place it on a large plate on a bed of lettuce. Garnish with lemon slices, salmon on toast with the caviar, slices of egg and capers. Sprinkle lobster with the bread crumbs.

…serve a chablis with this (the same one used in cooking).

Jan A. Oudendijk – Kahala Hilton Hotel
Honolulu, Hawaii

le homard grille breton
à la crème d'estragon

3 live, 1-1/2-pound lobsters
8 chopped shallots
1 cup clarified butter
3 ounces fresh butter
2 cups fresh cream
1 cup chopped fresh tarragon
1-1/2 cups white wine (sancerre
    or muscadet)
1/2 cup brandy
3 ounces grated gruyere cheese
salt, pepper, cayenne

Split the lobsters in two lengthwise. Remove the sack behind the head, and
the thin line running from the head through the body and tail. Detach the claws
and crack them. Place the halved lobsters and claws together in a roasting pan.
Season with salt, pepper, and cayenne and sprinkle with the clarified butter.
Cook in a pre-heated oven at 400° for about 15-20 minutes, basting the
lobsters with the pan juices. Remove from the oven and place the lobster pieces
on a serving dish. Sprinkle with brandy, and keep warm while making the sauce.

Drain off the pan juice, heat 1 tablespoon of butter and cook the shallots until
they are golden (not brown). Add the remaining brandy and flame it. Pour
in the white wine and reduce to half. Stir in the fresh cream and the fresh
tarragon and cook for about 5 minutes. Remove from the stove. Add two tablespoons of fresh butter while stirring constantly. When thick and smooth, pour the
sauce over the lobsters. Sprinkle the half lobsters lightly with cheese and place
under the salamander until golden. Serve very hot.

Ed Sullivan – Honolulu, Hawaii
Hyatt Regency, Waikiki

buzz's shrimp aulike

2-1/2 pounds shrimp (26-30 size)
1/2 cup celery tops
3-1/2 teaspoons salt
1/2 cup mixed pickling spices
onion
7 bay leaves

sauce:

1-1/2 cups salad oil
3/4 cup white wine
1-1/2 teaspoons salt
2-1/2 teaspoons celery seed
2-1/2 tablespoons capers and juice
dash of Tabasco sauce

Add the shrimp, celery tops, 3-1/2 teaspoons salt and mixed pickling spices to a pot of boiling water. Cook until shrimp turn opaque, about 5 minutes – don't overcook. Drain shrimp. Cool with cold water. Devein shrimp. Alternate shrimp and sliced round onions (1 pint) in a shallow dish. Add 7 or 8 bay leaves.

For the sauce, combine all ingredients and mix well. Pour over shrimp and onions. Cover and store in refrigerator at least 24 hours for best flavor. Keeps at least a week in refrigerator. Add whole olives…makes a fantastic pupu, and best of all, can be prepared ahead of time.

Bobbie Lou Schneider – Honolulu, Hawaii

shrimp maison

1-1/2 pounds fresh shrimp
1/2 cup Maui onion
2 tablespoons green onion
3 cups mushrooms
4 cloves fresh garlic
1/2 cup butter

1/2 cup dry white wine
3 tablespoons lemon juice
1/4 cup chopped parsley
1 teaspoon salt
1/4 teaspoon pepper

Cook shrimp as directed in Carson's shrimp (see page 129). Peel when cooled. Chop Maui onion and green onion. Thinly slice mushrooms and crush garlic. Melt butter until foaming. Stir in onions and cook 30 seconds. Stir in mushrooms and cook another 30 seconds. Stir in garlic and again cook for 30 seconds. Add shrimp and wine, simmer 2 minutes. Add lemon juice, parsley, salt and pepper, simmer 3 to 5 minutes. Serves 4 over rice.

Anne Oliver – Honolulu, Hawaii

shrimp curry

6 tablespoons butter
1 small onion
1 clove garlic
6 tablespoons flour
2-1/4 tablespoons curry powder
1/2 teaspoon salt
dash cayenne
3/4 cup beef broth
12-ounce can coconut milk
1 cup half and half
1/2 teaspoon lemon juice
1/2 green apple, grated
1-1/2 pounds shrimp

Clean and devein the shrimp. Melt butter, add chopped onion and chopped garlic and saute. Cook shrimp for 3 minutes and set aside. Stir in flour mixed with curry powder, salt and cayenne. Add beef broth, coconut milk, half and half, and lemon juice, stirring until smooth. Place over boiling water, add grated apple and shrimp and cook 20 minutes. Serve with cooked rice and condiments... green onions, grated egg, chutney, chopped peanuts, crumbled bacon, shredded coconut and raisins.

Shirley Connors – Honolulu, Hawaii

crabmeat au gratin

3 tablespoons butter
3 tablespoons flour
3/4 cup milk
3/4 cup whipping cream
1 teaspoon Worcestershire sauce
salt to taste
2 tablespoons gruyere cheese
2 tablespoons Parmesan cheese
2 tablespoons butter
dash of cayenne pepper
1 tablespoon sherry
3 cups crabmeat

Make cream sauce with butter, flour, milk and cream, (do not whip cream). Do not boil. When hot, add cheeses, Worcestershire, butter and sherry. Fold in crabmeat and put into individual ramekins. Sprinkle with additional Parmesan and boil until bubbly. Serves 3 to 4...very rich, small portions are better.

Betsy McVay – Honolulu, Hawaii

crab curry

1/4 cup chopped onion
1/2 clove garlic, mashed
1/4 cup butter (4 tablespoons)
2 teaspoons curry powder
2 tablespoons flour
2 cups light cream
1-1/2 pounds fresh crab, or
    3 cans, flaked
1/2 teaspoon salt
dash of cayenne
pinch of thyme
2 egg yolks
4 cups hot steamed rice
    (1-1/2 cups uncooked)
condiments: crumbled bacon, chopped
    salted peanuts, pickle relish

Saute onion and garlic in butter until limp but not browned. Add curry powder and cook over very low heat for 10 minutes. Blend in flour gradually and add cream gradually. Cook, stirring constantly until thickened. Remove from heat and strain into the top of a double boiler. Place sauce over boiling water and add crab, salt, cayenne and thyme. Cook until heated through.

Stir slightly beaten egg yolks into sauce and cook just until heated through. Spoon over hot rice, turned out on a hot plate and sprinkle with condiments. Serves 6-8.

…serve chutney with this, shredded coconut, green onions, bananas with lemon juice, also fruit salad, broiled tomatoes, hot rolls with currant jelly.

Sally Ritcheson – Oklahoma City, Oklahoma

deviled crab louisiane

1/8 pound margarine or 1/4 cup oil
1/2 cup chopped onion
1/2 cup chopped celery
1/8 cup minced green onion
1 clove minced garlic
1/4 teaspoon Worcestershire sauce
1/2 pound crabmeat chunks
1/2 teaspoon white wine vinegar
salt, black pepper and red pepper
     to taste
1/8 cup chopped green onion tops
2 tablespoons chopped parsley
1/4 package stale buns – soaked in water
1/2 cup evaporated milk or heavy cream
2 eggs

Put oil or margarine in a heavy pot. When oil becomes hot, saute chopped onions, celery, green pepper and garlic until wilted. Add Worcestershire sauce, crab meat and vinegar. Stir thoroughly and season lightly with salt, black pepper and red pepper. Cook over medium heat for about 15 minutes, stirring constantly. Add onion tops and parsley. Wring out soaked buns and break up in pan, along with milk or cream and eggs. Mix well, and season to taste again using salt, black pepper and red pepper. Fill crab shells or casseroles. Sprinkle with bread crumbs and paprika. Bake in oven at 325° for 10 to 15 minutes. Serve hot with french bread. Serves 4.

Jacque Orenstein – Oklahoma City, Oklahoma
Creative Cookery

crabmeat casserole

1 package medium noodles
2 cans crabmeat
1/2 pound pimento cheese, grated
1/4 pound butter
1 cup cream

Melt butter and cheese in a double boiler. Add cream and crabmeat. Boil noodles and add to mixture. Pour mixture into a casserole dish. Add grated cheese on top. Bake at 350° for 30 minutes.

Evelyn Nordquist – Honolulu, Hawaii

crabmeat enchiladas

salad oil
16 6-inch corn tortillas
1 cup sour cream
1 bunch scallions, thinly sliced

enchilada sauce

6 tablespoons butter
6 tablespoons flour
3 10-ounce cans mild red chili
    enchilada sauce
2-1/4 cups chicken broth
1/4 teaspoon crushed dried oregano
1/2 teaspoon cumin

Melt butter in heavy skillet over low heat. Add flour. Cook 2 minutes, stirring
often. Remove from heat, let cool 1 minute. Stir in enchilada sauce and broth.
Return to heat. Bring sauce to a simmer while stirring with wire whisk. Add
spices. Simmer gently, stirring often, for 5 to 8 minutes or until sauce thickens.
Remove from heat, set aside, covered.

crabmeat filling

1 pound crabmeat, picked over
    and flaked
1 pound Monterey Jack cheese,
    coarsely grated
1 bunch scallions, thinly sliced

Combine all ingredients in a bowl and mix until well blended.

To assemble enchiladas…in a small, heavy skillet, heat about 1/4 inch of oil over
moderate heat. Dip one tortilla at a time in the hot oil for a few seconds to
soften. Then dip it into the enchilada sauce. Stack tortillas. Spoon some filling
down the center of each. Fold one side over filling and roll into a cylinder. Arrange
seam side down, and slightly apart in an 8 x 13 ovenproof dish. Reheat
remaining sauce and ladle over tortillas.

Bake uncovered in a preheated oven at 350° for 20 minutes or until cheese
in filling is melted and sauce bubbles. Top each enchilada with a dollop of sour
cream and sprinkle with sliced scallions.

Susie Judycki – Red River, New Mexico

imperial prawns

4 tablespoons sunflower oil
6 cloves garlic
1-1/2 inches fresh ginger (chunk)
2 tablespoons black beans (Chinese)
3 pounds jumbo prawns, cleaned
1/2 bunch fresh scallions
2 jiggers gin
3 tablespoons soy sauce
1/2 bunch Chinese parsley

Heat Chinese wok, spatula and oil over high flame. Crush garlic, ginger, and black beans and heat in wok. Add prawns, scallions, soy sauce and gin, and stir for 15 to 20 minutes. When ready to serve, garnish with Chinese parsley. Serves 10.

John Young – Honolulu, Hawaii

cassola de peix

(seafood casserole)

2 tablespoons butter or margarine
2 tablespoons all purpose flour
1/4 teaspoon salt
1 cup milk
12 medium shrimp, cooked and split
    or 1 4-1/2-ounce can shrimp
1-1/2 cups fresh crabmeat or
    1 7-1/2-ounce can crabmeat
1 cup steamed lobster, or
    1 5-1/2-ounce can lobster
1 3-ounce can mushrooms, sliced
2 tablespoons sherry
1 tablespoon lemon juice
dash of Tabasco sauce
1/4 teaspoon Worcestershire sauce
4 hard boiled eggs
1/2 cup shredded sharp cheese
1 cup soft bread crumbs
2 tablespoons butter or margarine,
    melted

Melt butter over low heat. Blend in flour and salt. Add milk all at once. Cook quickly, stirring constantly, until sauce thickens and bubbles. Then remove from heat.

Add next 8 ingredients and mix well. Line a quart casserole with sliced hard boiled eggs. Place mixture in the dish and sprinkle cheese on top. Combine bread crumbs and melted butter. Sprinkle over cheese. Bake at 375° for 40 minutes.

Sally's grandmother – Alzada Black – Ponca City, Oklahoma

crab luncheon

1 can king crabmeat
2 3-ounce packages cream cheese
1 tablespoon onion juice
1 tablespoon catsup
1 tablespoon mayonnaise
1 tablespoon Worcestershire sauce
6 tomato slices
6 English muffin halves

Mix crab, cheese, onion juice, catsup, mayonnaise and Worcestershire sauce, and let marinate. Butter muffins and place a slice of tomato on each. Add crab mixture. Bake at 350° for 30 minutes. Serves 6.

Marilyn Goss – Honolulu, Hawaii

carson's shrimp

1 bottle of beer plus enough water to cover shrimp.

Add beer to water and bring to a boil. Add shrimp and bring to a full boil. Set aside for 1 minute. Drain, cover with cold water to stop cooking. Drain again, then refrigerate. Serve with shrimp sauce.

Carson Bell – Aspen, Colorado

…Carson served this to his daughters Shawna and Leslie, when his wife Barbara was out of town. Says Carson…"you just spread out newspaper on the kitchen table, pour the chilled shrimp into the middle of the paper, and let the children go at it. The girls loved it and this dinner saves time on clean up, …just roll up the newspaper when they are finished and throw it away. You've got full, satisfied children, and a clean kitchen for your wife to come home to!"

seafood etouffe

1 bell pepper, chopped
1-1/2 cups chopped celery
2 onions, chopped
1 stick of butter
1 can cream of mushroom soup
1 can cream of celery soup
1/2 can tomato soup
1 pound crab meat
4 to 5 pounds shrimp
garlic, salt and pepper

In a large skillet, melt 1/2 stick butter and brown celery, onion and bell pepper. Then transfer to a large deep pot. Peel and de-vein the shrimp and saute the shrimp and crab with the remainder of butter and seasoning to taste, transferring to pot when shrimp becomes pink. Add all the soup to the pot. Simmer until ready to serve.

Serve over rice, with a green salad and garlic french bread.

Jane Morris – Ponca City, Oklahoma

marjoram

marjoram

Mediterranean origin...its aromatic
scent and flavor are, according to legend,
said to have come from the delicate touch
of Venus who grew it on Mt. Olympus,
and imparted to it a lasting aroma as a
reminder to all of her beauty...it
is a relative to both the oregano and
mint families.

Beef & Veal

veal liver with xeres vinegar

sauce

2 soup spoons chopped shallots
2 soup spoons xeres vinegar
2 soup spoons fresh cream
2 soup spoons brown sauce
1 soup spoon chopped parsley
3 ounces fresh butter
flour
2 pounds calf's liver

Heat 1 ounce butter in frying pan. Add salt and pepper on liver slices, then dredge in flour. Saute for 3 minutes on both sides. Remove from pan and keep warm.

Add shallots, cover pan and cook for 2 minutes. Add vinegar, brown sauce and 2 ounces butter and fresh cream. Cook for 3 minutes, then add the chopped parsley.

Pour sauce over veal liver slices. Serve with fresh pommes purée (mashed potatoes). Serves 4.

…xeres vinegar is a sherry vinegar.

Fred Hellekes
Liberty House – Honolulu, Hawaii

cold veal meatloaf with brioche

1 pound veal, ground
1 pound pork, ground
1/4 cup onion, chopped
2 carrots, finely grated
1 teaspoon thyme
1-1/2 teaspoons salt
1/2 teaspoon black pepper
1/2 cup sour cream
1 egg

Mix all ingredients together well and place in a 9 x 5 x 3-inch loaf pan. Bake at 350° for 1-1/2 hours. When cool, remove from pan and chill. Prepare the brioche and allow to chill. (See brioche recipe below)

When the veal loaf has been wrapped in the brioche, brush with beaten egg and bake at 400° for 20 minutes, or until nicely browned. Allow to chill well before serving. Serve with assorted mustards.

brioche

1 package yeast
1/4 cup warm water
1 teaspoon sugar
3/4 cup frozen butter
2 cups flour
1 teaspoon salt
2 eggs

Combine the yeast, water and sugar. Allow to proof. Cut butter into small pieces. Place the butter, flour and salt in the food processor, fitted with the steel blade. Blend until the mixture is crumbly. Add the yeast and mix until the flour is moistened. Add the eggs. Blend until dough is smooth. If the dough sticks before it is blended well enough, add a tablespoon of flour to pull the dough away from the sides of the beaker. Place the smooth dough in a bowl and cover with plastic and allow to double in volume. Shape the dough into 1 large or 8 small brioche. Allow to double in size and place in a pre-heated oven for the times indicated below. If a glossy brown crust is desired, brush the loaves with beaten egg.

large – 375° 45 minutes
small – 375° 20-25 minutes

Lavonne Tollerud – Honolulu, Hawaii

vitello tonnato

3-4 pounds veal from the leg, tied up
    securely
1 large onion, sliced
10 fillets anchovy, drained (1 can)
1 can tuna packed in oil, drained
2 glasses white wine
1/3 cup olive oil
1 pint chicken stock
2 cloves garlic
4 stalks celery
1 carrot
dash of thyme
couple of sprigs of parsley
salt and pepper
mayonnaise
lemon juice

Heat oil in a heavy kettle and brown veal on all sides. Add all the other ingredients
except mayonnaise and lemon juice. Cook, covered, very slowly until meat can be
pierced easily with a fork. Allow meat to cool in stock. Refrigerate meat (overnight).
Cook down stock to about 1/2. Force through a coarse sieve. Chill and remove
any fat.

For the sauce, add mayonnaise to the stock, beating with a whisk. Do it gradually
until sauce is consistency of very heavy cream. Add juice of 1 lemon. The finished
sauce should cling to the meat slice.

To serve, spread a thick layer of yellow rice (add turmeric to rice water) on a platter.
Arrange thin slices of veal on rice. Surround with tomato slices. Pour on sauce.
Sprinkle with drained capers. Serve extra sauce on the side.

...If you can't get rump of veal in Hawaii, you can be sneaky and use a whole
rolled breast of turkey, but it won't be as good.

George Lazarnick – Honolulu, Hawaii

diced veal à la suisse

1-1/2 pounds veal fillets, thin
1 small onion
4 tablespoons cooking oil
3 tablespoons butter
1/4 cup dry white wine
3/4 cup heavy cream
2 teaspoons parsley
1/2 cube chicken bouillon
sprinkle of flour and paprika
salt and pepper to taste

Dice veal into bite-size pieces, sprinkle lightly with flour. Put half the oil into a skillet. When it is hot, add half of the veal, turning constantly for about 1-1/2 minutes, then remove to a bowl with a slotted spoon. Do the same with remaining oil and veal. When done, pour out any excess oil and add 2 tablespoons butter. Over medium heat, saute finely chopped onion until golden yellow, then add wine and bouillon cube.

Cook until reduced by half, then add veal and any remaining juices which have collected in the bowl. Reheat for 1 minute longer, swirl in the rest of the butter. Salt and pepper, sprinkle with paprika and chopped parsley.

Serve immediately with a dry, savory rice.

Heidi Bachmann – Honolulu, Hawaii

veal saute

2-1/2 pounds veal, cut into cubes
flour, salt and pepper
1/4 cup olive oil
1 teaspoon paprika
1/2 cup chopped green onions
1 teaspoon thyme
1 cup white wine
1/2 cup water
12 small white onions, peeled
mushrooms

Dredge veal in flour seasoned with salt and pepper and brown in olive oil, sprinkling with a little paprika as it cooks. Add green onions, thyme, wine and water. Cover and simmer gently for 40 minutes. Add onions and mushrooms and simmer until tender and meat is cooked through. Serves 4.

...I use canned small white onions.

Evelyn Nordquist – Honolulu, Hawaii

136

breast of veal

5-pound breast of veal
2 tablespoons butter

mirepoix of vegetables:
     2 cups chopped onions
     2 cups chopped celery
     2 cups chopped carrot

1 cup Noilly Prat vermouth
1 cup chicken or veal stock
1 teaspoon marjoram
salt and pepper

Brown veal in butter in a large pan that has a cover. When brown, remove to a platter and put the mirepoix of vegetables in the pan and cook until golden. Add salt, pepper and marjoram and mix thoroughly. Pour on the vermouth and allow to boil for 1 minute. Add the stock and return meat to pan, sprinkling with more salt and pepper.

Cover and allow to cook very slowly for 1-1/2 to 2 hours. Pour off the liquid and put in freezer to chill quickly. Remove fat (this isn't really necessary as there is very little fat). Make a roux of 2 tablespoons butter and 2 tablespoons flour to thicken broth. Serve with buttered noodles and some of the mirepoix.

Verna Lazarnick – Honolulu, Hawaii

danish veal casserole

1-3/4 pounds stewing veal
2 to 3 ounces butter
2 large onions
pepper, paprika and a pinch of thyme
bouquet garni
1-1/4 cups stock
8 ounces mushrooms, sliced
cornflour
chopped parsley

Cut meat into cubes and fry in butter in saucepan until browned. Add finely chopped onion and cook until golden. Add all ingredients except mushrooms, pour in the stock and cook for 1 hour on low heat. Then add mushrooms and cook for 5 minutes. Thicken the gravy with cornflour. Garnish with parsley.
Serves 4.

…Serve with rice or potatoes.

Osa Nielsen – Honolulu, Hawaii

individual beef wellingtons

6 5-ounce fillets of beef
vegetable oil
salt and pepper
1 cup chopped mushrooms
1 clove garlic, minced
2 tablespoons butter
1 small tin (2-1/4-ounce) paté de foie gras
2 10-ounce packages frozen puff pastry shells, thawed
1 egg, beaten

Season fillets with salt and pepper and sear in a little oil on both sides for a few minutes. Cool and chill. Saute garlic and mushrooms in butter and season with salt and pepper to taste. Top each fillet with a little paté and mushroom mixture; chill for 30 minutes. Roll out patty shells, using 1-1/2 shells to wrap each fillet, using remaining pastry for design on top. Brush top and sides of each with egg and bake at 400° for 12 minutes – rare, 16 minutes – medium and 20 minutes – well done.

…This can be prepared ahead and refrigerated for a few hours…serve with bearnaise sauce.

Barbara Bell – Aspen, Colorado

tenderloin deluxe

2 tablespoons softened butter
2 pounds whole beef tenderloin
2 tablespoons butter
1/4 cup chopped green onion
2 tablespoons soy sauce
1 teaspoon Dijon mustard
dash of freshly ground pepper
3/4 cup sherry

Spread softened butter on tenderloin and place on foil-lined baking pan. Bake uncovered at 400° for 20 minutes.

In a saucepan, melt 2 tablespoons butter and saute green onion until tender. Add soy sauce, mustard, pepper and sherry and heat until boiling. Pour sauce over meat and bake an additional 20-25 minutes. Baste frequently with sauce from pan.

Carve into 8 slices and serve. Serves 4.

Carol Collins – San Francisco, California

baked steak

1 3-inch thick sirloin steak (approximately 6 pounds)
1 large sweet onion, grated or finely chopped
5 tablespoons butter
1-1/4 cups chili sauce (Heinz)
4 tablespoons Worcestershire sauce
1 pound small mushrooms, washed and halved
1 clove garlic
1 cup heavy cream
salt and pepper

Place steak under broiler and sear 7 minutes on each side. Reserve drippings. While steak is searing, prepare steak sauce by heating together 3 tablespoons butter, 1 cup chili sauce, 3 tablespoons Worcestershire sauce and grated onion. Remove steak from broiler, pour sauce over it and bake 45-50 minutes at 350°.

To make the mushroom sauce, cut garlic clove in half and rub large frying pan with it. Melt 2 tablespoons butter in pan, add mushrooms and saute, covered, for 5 minutes. Then add 1 tablespoon Worcestershire sauce, 1/4 cup chili sauce, 1 cup heavy cream, and 5 tablespoons drippings from steak. Season with salt and pepper, cook for 5 minutes. Serve with steak.

Barbara Bell – Aspen, Colorado

oven bar-b-que

5-pound boneless chuck roast
1 6-ounce can whole peeled tomatoes
1 large onion, chopped
1 cup chopped celery
1 tablespoon hot salsa
1 small can chopped green chiles
1 teaspoon pepper
3/4 teaspoon garlic salt
1/2 teaspoon salt

Set roast in a large roasting pan. Combine tomatoes, onion, celery, salsa, green chiles, pepper, garlic and salt. Pour over roast and let stand in refrigerator overnight.

Cook, covered, at 275° for 12 hours. Remove from oven and shred with a fork. Serve on hot onion rolls. Makes 25 sandwiches. You may add bar-b-que sauce.

Doris Mires – Ponca City, Oklahoma

gourmet style flank steak

3/4 pound flank steak
1/2 pound butter
1/2 bulb garlic, diced finely
1/4 bunch parsley, diced finely
3 ounces fresh green onions, diced
3 ounces chives, diced
3-ounce wedge bleu cheese
1 pint bleu cheese dressing
salt and pepper and any optional
     choice of seasoning
paprika

For easy serving, prepare in advance: Saute diced garlic in butter, do not burn, set aside. Wrap separately diced parsley and chives, set aside. Crumble cheese wedge to chunky consistency and add dressing.

Broil flank steak on barbecue grill only until very rare, season with salt and pepper.

Timing is now important…when you have broiled your steak very rare, add the diced parsley to your preheated garlic butter. Slice flank steak London broil style into thin slices diagonally, against the grain of the meat. Lay the slices on a serving platter overlapping each other, forming the same shape as the original flank steak. Mix the garlic and parsley butter well and spoon in between the slices. Place under oven broiler for one to three minutes, long enough to bring the meat to medium rare. Do not overcook. Spoon the cheese mixture over the flank steak and sprinkle with chives and paprika.

Note…for a family style centerpiece, with the flank steak placed in the middle of the serving platter, surround it with overlapping slices of cucumber and tomato, garnish with parsley, radishes and any other colorful vegetables of your choice.

Howard Picard – St. Louis, Missouri
Stuart Anderson's Cattle Company

entrecote bordelaise

4 rib eye or club steaks
3 to 4 tablespoons butter
1 to 2 tablespoons oil
salt and pepper

sauce bordelaise

2 tablespoons minced shallots
1 cup red wine
1/8 teaspoon crushed thyme
1/8 teaspoon crushed peppercorns
1 tablespoon beurre manie (1 tablespoon
   butter plus 1 teaspoon flour)

Melt butter and oil over a moderately hot fire (preferably an iron skillet) until it begins to color. Add steaks which have been well dried, and saute over high heat for 4 minutes on each side for medium rare. Remove steaks to a heated platter and keep warm while finishing sauce. Salt meat after cooking.

For sauce, saute the shallots in the pan juices until golden, then add the red wine, pepper and thyme and cook over moderate high heat until the liquid has reduced by one-half. Add the "beurre manie" (take 1 tablespoon soft butter and roll into a ball with 1 teaspoon flour) to the pan juices and stir over low heat for a minute or two. This will thicken the sauce slightly. Taste for seasoning and add 1 tablespoon butter if the sauce is too acid. Pour over steaks and serve immediately.

Helen L. Frost – Wichita Falls, Texas

st. paul's burgers à la wallace edwards

1 pound lean ground beef
3 eggs
1/2 green pepper
1/2 onion
salt, pepper, garlic powder

In a large bowl combine beef, beaten eggs, chopped green pepper, chopped onion, salt, pepper and garlic. Mix well and make into large patties. Pan fry slowly or broil. Makes 4 patties.

Wallace Edwards – Ponca City, Oklahoma

argentine rolled beef

2 flank steaks, 2 pounds each
1 cup fresh peas, corn and carrots
    or substitute frozen mixed
    vegetables – thawed
1/2 cup onion, finely chopped
1/4 cup green pepper, chopped
2 teaspoons chili powder
1/4 cup finely chopped pimento
1 clove garlic
1 teaspoon salt
1 celery stalk
1 onion
1 cup beef broth
1 carrot ·
1 clove garlic, chopped
chili sauce (recipe next page)

Preheat oven to 350°.

Butterfly steaks by using a long sharp knife and slit the flank steak lengthwise, almost cutting through. Do not cut all the way through. Open the flank steak and pound it thoroughly with a meat pounder, as thin as possible. All excess fat should be trimmed so that the finished steak is roughly square, about 12 x 12 inches. Lay the two steaks side by side, overlapping the edges about 2 inches, so when you roll them they hold together like one piece of meat.

Combine the mixed vegetables, chopped onion, chopped green pepper, pimento, chili powder, crushed garlic and salt, mix thoroughly. Spread this mixture evenly over the steaks, covering the entire surface. Roll the two steaks up, jelly roll fashion, as tight as possible. Tie the roll securely every two inches, using five lengths of thread or string.

Place the roll in a shallow casserole (clay cookers are ideal). Add beef broth, sliced celery, sliced carrot, sliced onion and chopped garlic. Cover and bake for 2 hours, basting the meat several times. Move the meat to a platter about 15 minutes before serving. This will make the meat firmer and easier to carve. Slice the meat in about 1-1/2-inch slices and serve with chili sauce (see next page).

chili sauce

4 tablespoons butter
1 onion
1 green pepper
1 clove garlic
2 tablespoons flour
1 tablespoon chili powder
1 teaspoon salt
freshly ground black pepper
1 cup tomato juice
1 cup beef broth

Melt butter in a medium sized skillet. Add finely chopped onions, green peppers and minced garlic. Saute for 5 minutes, stirring frequently until vegetables are translucent, not browned. Blend in the flour, chili powder, salt and pepper. Stir over low heat for 2 minutes. Stir in tomato juice and beef broth. Cook, stirring over medium heat until slightly thickened. Serve hot.

Cliff C. Henderson – Richardson, Texas

beef and radishes

From a Chinese cookbook written by Julia's mother, Mary Sia.

1 teaspoon cornstarch
2 tablespoons soy sauce
1/2 pound beef, sliced
4 tablespoons oil
1 tablespoon cornstarch
1/2 cup sugar
1/3 cup vinegar
4 tablespoons water
1-1/2 cups radishes, peeled,
    sliced crosswise
1/4 cup chopped green onions

Combine cornstarch and soy sauce. Add to beef and mix well. Heat pan and add oil. Add mixture of cornstarch, sugar, vinegar and water and bring to a boil. Add radishes and simmer until they become transparent. Stir in beef and marinade and simmer briefly, about 3 seconds. Add green onions and stir 1 second. Serves 4.

…Asparagus may be used in place of radishes.

Julia Ing – Honolulu, Hawaii

beef chofleur

1 pound boneless round steak
1 small head cauliflower
2 tablespoons butter or margarine
1 green pepper, cut in 3/4-inch pieces
1/4 cup soy sauce
1 clove garlic, minced
2 tablespoons cornstarch
1/2 teaspoon sugar
1-1/2 cups beef broth or water
1 cup sliced green onions, with tops
3 cups hot cooked rice

Cut meat into 1/2-inch squares. Separate cauliflower into flowerettes. Brown meat in butter about 5 minutes and then add cauliflower, green pepper, soy sauce and garlic. Stir lightly to coat vegetables with soy sauce. Cover pan and simmer until vegetables are barely tender, about 10 minutes.

Blend cornstarch, sugar and beef broth, add to meat mixture with green onions. Cook, stirring constantly until thoroughly heated and sauce is thickened. Serve over hot beds of fluffy rice. Serves 4-6.

Janet Schiller – Honolulu, Hawaii

keema

1 onion
1 clove garlic
3 tablespoons butter
1 pound ground beef
1 tablespoon curry powder
1 teaspoon salt
dash of pepper
2 large tomatoes
2 potatoes
1 package frozen peas

Chop onion and garlic finely, then saute in butter. Remove from pan. Fry ground beef in skillet until browned. Combine onion, garlic and meat with diced tomatoes, diced potatoes, frozen peas, curry powder, salt and pepper. Simmer for approximately 25 minutes. Serves 4.

Celia Tenby – Honolulu, Hawaii

papa's matambre with three sauces

1 3-pound flank steak
1/4 cup red wine
1/4 cup vinegar
2 teaspoons thyme
1 head garlic, minced
1 large onion, chopped
1 large pimento, chopped
2 carrots, parboiled
2 gherkins (sweet pickles), sliced
1/2 pound ground veal
1 bunch fresh spinach, washed and drained
3 hard boiled eggs

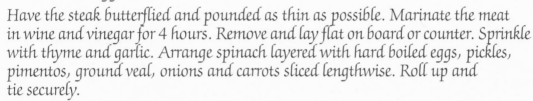

Have the steak butterflied and pounded as thin as possible. Marinate the meat in wine and vinegar for 4 hours. Remove and lay flat on board or counter. Sprinkle with thyme and garlic. Arrange spinach layered with hard boiled eggs, pickles, pimentos, ground veal, onions and carrots sliced lengthwise. Roll up and tie securely.

Put into a casserole dish and pour 2 tablespoons of olive oil over the top. Cook, covered, at 350°. Baste every 15 minutes for a cooking time of 1-1/2 hours. When cooked, remove from oven and cool for 10 minutes before slicing. Serve with mustard, chili and garlic and parsley sauces (see sauces). Serves 6.

Lilia Lee – Honolulu, Hawaii

bourbon stew

1 ounce bourbon
1 pound beef
2 tablespoons cooking oil
1 cup consomme
1 large onion
2 carrots
2 large potatoes
2 tablespoons flour
salt and pepper to taste

Cut vegetables in small cubes. Set aside. Chop meat in small cubes. Mix flour with salt and pepper. Place oil in heavy pan and heat. Roll meat in seasoned flour and brown on all sides. Add consomme and onion, simmer. Add carrots and potatoes last. Add bourbon and simmer till done.

Anne G. Swan – Honolulu, Hawaii

boeuf de français

1/4 cup butter
1 medium onion, chopped
1/2 cup diced celery
1 4-ounce can sliced mushrooms,
    drained well
2 cups soft breadcrumbs
1 teaspoon salt
1/8 teaspoon black pepper
1/2 teaspoon basil leaves
1/8 teaspoon parsley flakes
5 pounds beef tenderloin, trimmed
4 slices bacon

Melt butter in a small skillet over low heat. Add onion, celery and mushrooms and saute until onion is soft and transparent, about 10 minutes. Place bread crumbs in a 1-quart bowl. Add salt, pepper, basil leaves and parsley flakes, melted butter and onion mixture. Lightly mix until well blended. Make a lengthwise cut 3/4 of the way through the tenderloin. Place the stuffing lightly in the pocket formed by the cut. Close the pocket by fastening meat together with wooden toothpicks. Place bacon strips diagonally across the top, covering the picks and the pocket. Place stuffed meat in an oblong dish or pan. Bake, uncovered, in a 350° oven for one hour and 20 minutes for medium rare. Serves 8.

Marylou Brogan – Honolulu, Hawaii

teriyaki

2 16-ounce pieces prime New York strip steak
1/2 cup soy sauce
1/2 cup sake or cooking sherry
1 head garlic, minced
2 tablespoons fresh ginger, minced
1/2 cup scallions, sliced very fine
1/2 cup brown sugar or honey
1/2 teaspoon black pepper
2 teaspoons or more arrowroot for marinade thickening

Stir all ingredients for marinade together and simmer in a saucepan for 10 minutes. Do not boil. Reserve 1 cup for sauce.

Place meat in a glass dish and pour marinade over it. Refrigerate for 8 hours. Charcoal broil meat or cook in oven broiler to degree desired.

In a saucepan, pour reserved sauce and add arrowroot mixture. Stir until thick… pour immediately on meat and serve. Serves 4.

…mushroom garnish is optional.

                    Julia Wood – Honolulu, Hawaii

mertzburgers

1 pound ground round
1 tablespoon cooking oil
1 large onion
1 green pepper
1 teaspoon garlic powder
1 tablespoon chili powder
1 can tomato soup
1 heaping tablespoon flour

Brown ground round in cooking oil add onion and green pepper and continue to cook, keep stirring. Add chili powder and garlic powder, stir. Add flour, stir. Add soup, mix well and bring to boil for one or two minutes or until bubbly. Serve on hamburger buns.

                    Hattie Mertz, Ponca City, Oklahoma

miniature meat loaves

1 pound ground beef
3/4 cup Nabisco 100% bran cereal
1/3 cup onion, chopped
1 teaspoon dry mustard
2 teaspoons Worcestershire sauce
1 teaspoon salt
1/8 teaspoon pepper
1 egg, slightly beaten
1/2 cup water

glaze

2 tablespoons apricot preserves
1 teaspoon vinegar
1/2 teaspoon Worcestershire sauce

For the meat loaves, combine all ingredients and form into 4 loaves. Place in a 13 x 9 x 2-inch casserole and top with with glaze.

To make the glaze, mix preserves, vinegar and Worcestershire sauce together. After spooning glaze over loaves, bake at 400° for 25 minutes or longer if desired.

Maxine Thomas – Honolulu, Hawaii

arthur's hamburgers

"I like rare, broiled hamburgers," said Arthur Murray. "But when they are broiled in a patty, the middle stays rare, but the outer portion becomes too well done."

He went on:
"…take 4 to 4-1/2 ounces chopped ground round, form it into a doughnut shape. When the meat has reached room temperature, turn on the broiler to high heat and place the rack as close to the heat as possible.

I use ground black pepper on both sides of the meat, no salt. After pre-heating the broiler for 15 minutes, broil the meat for 1 and 1/2 minutes on each side.

You can fill the center when serving with warmed relish or catsup, or catsup mixed with mustard. Try a doughnut hamburger!"

Arthur Murray – Honolulu, Hawaii

enchiladas a' aspen

filling

1-1/2 pounds ground beef
1/2 cup Longhorn cheese
1/2 cup green onion tops
2 cloves garlic
salt and pepper

sauce

1 small jar pimentos
1 small can green chopped chiles
1 can cream of mushroom soup
3/4 can evaporated milk
1 package green onion dip
3/4 pound Velveeta cheese

Saute ground beef until brown. Add shredded cheese and blend well. Add chopped onions, finely chopped garlic, and salt and pepper.

For the sauce, heat all the ingredients to melting in a double boiler.

Heat the tortillas in Crisco oil. Drain, and fill with beef mixture. Put in a casserole dish and cover with sauce. Heat at 325° until sauce bubbles. Serves 12.

Pat Van de Mark – Aspen, Colorado

never fail rib roast

...this recipe was given to the Sam Cookes by Mrs. C.M. Cooke, III, his mother. It works for any size roast as long as it is a standing rib with bone in.

Preheat oven to 375°. Roast should be at room temperature, so be sure it is defrosted and out of the refrigerator at least 3 hours.

Rub the roast with white pepper and place in oven for 1 hour...then turn off the heat and tape door shut with sign: DO NOT OPEN DOOR.

One and a half hours before serving, turn oven on to 300° for 50 minutes. Remove roast from oven and allow to sit for 30 minutes before carving. Do the initial hour of roasting in the morning and finish up 2 hours before serving time.

Mary Cooke – Honolulu, Hawaii

beef stew

1/2 pound salt pork
2 pounds beef
2 tablespoons flour
salt and pepper

sauce

1-1/2 cloves garlic, minced
1 cup beef bouillon
12 peppercorns
3 tablespoons Worcestershire sauce
1 bay leaf
1 large onion, chopped
8 ounces tomato sauce (1 cup)
6 whole cloves
1/4 cup chopped parsley
1/2 cup sherry

vegetables

6 medium potatoes, peeled and quartered
6 carrots, quartered
2 stalks celery, chopped
1 can sliced mushrooms
1 green pepper, sliced thin or chopped

Cut the salt pork into small pieces, and the beef into pieces suitable for stewing. Saute pork over low heat. Brown stew meat in drippings over high heat, quickly, and sprinkle meat with salt, pepper and flour.

Combine all ingredients for sauce except sherry, and heat until boiling. Place the meat in a heavy saucepan. Pour the tomato mixture over it and simmer, closely covered for 4 hours. After 3-1/2 hours, add sherry. Cook the vegetables separately until tender. Add vegetables for the last 15 minutes of cooking. Serves 6.

Pat Evans – Ponca City, Oklahoma

oklahoma chili

2 pounds red beans
1 pound salt pork
2 pounds round steak
4 pounds ground beef
3 large Spanish onions
2 large green bell peppers
2-1/2 long green peppers
3 small hot chili peppers
6 large cloves garlic
8 pinches oregano
2 tablespoons cumin seed
1 teaspoon paprika
1 tablespoon parsley
3 tablespoons shortening
salt – to taste
cayenne – optional
1 15-ounce can tomato sauce
1 6-ounce can tomato paste
1/4 cup red wine

Soak beans overnight. Put beans in a large pot and cover with water. Cut salt pork into cubes and add to beans. Bring to a boil and simmer, adding water as needed. Cook for 1 to 1-1/2 hours, until done.

Chop onions and bell peppers coarsely, and chop hot chili peppers very fine. Smash garlic cloves and set all vegetables aside. Trim off fat from round steak and cut against the grain into 2-inch pieces. Heat shortening in a large pan, then cook steak until well browned on all sides. Add onions, peppers, garlic and the ground meat. Add seasonings.

When meat is no longer pink, add tomato sauce and paste. Add 1/2 of the cooked beans with liquid included and simmer for 3 hours. Skim off fat on top from time to time. As water evaporates, add more as needed. Re-season with oregano, cumin, parsley, and salt to taste. Use plenty of seasoning. If chili isn't hot enough, add cayenne. Pour in red wine and simmer until well blended.

Sugar and Spice

Tarragon

tarragon

Asian, Mongolian origin…given the name "tarkum" (dragon) by the famed thirteenth century Arab pharmacist in Spain, Ibn Baithar, because of its twisting, serpentine roots, this herb was unknown in ancient times…by now it has been adopted for a variety of uses, especially in the famous French "sauce bernaise" and in vinegar.

Poultry

idiot's chicken

Dear Sally,

I have a recurrent nightmare: my husband calls from the office to say he's bringing a guest home in an hour for dinner. The guest is Julia Child.

I mentioned my bad dream to Julia when I finally met her and she dismissed it with the remark: "I have a recipe that even an idiot can prepare."

Here it is…buy 2-1/2 pounds of drumsticks and thighs. Saute them in butter and oil until brown. Don't dredge the chicken in flour. The French dredge only rivers. When nicely browned, put in a medium-sized, thinly sliced onion and a touch of tarragon. Salt and pepper the chicken. Cover the pan…no water please. Cook at low heat about 20 minutes. Turn and baste chicken occasionally. And in the last 5 minutes of cooking, put in quartered, fresh mushrooms. When the chicken is tender, add 1/2 cup of dry white French vermouth (Noilly Prat is fine). Boil it down rapidly until almost syrupy. Add 2/3 cup of heavy cream and boil that down rapidly so that just enough is left to cover the chicken.

Serve with salad, rice and buttered asparagus tips. A superb dinner in 40 minutes.

Love,
Cobey
Cobey Black – Honolulu, Hawaii

monte's tabasco fried chicken

...from the McIlhenny Archives on Avery Island. They own Tabasco.

1 frying chicken, cut into serving pieces
milk
2 tablespoons Tabasco
6 tablespoons flour
6 tablespoons butter
6 tablespoons oil
salt, freshly ground pepper and
    Tabasco

In a bowl, cover cut-up chicken with the milk. Add Tabasco and salt. Allow to soak several hours or overnight. Remove chicken and roll in flour. Heat butter and oil in a heavy skillet until hot and fry chicken, skin side down, until well browned. Turn and brown on other side. Cover. Simmer for 10 minutes. Remove cover and crisp up in oil. Drain on paper towels.

Priscilla Growney – Kamuela, Hawaii

chicken rolls

8 chicken breasts (boned and skinned)
2 cups ricotta
1 package gruyere cheese
2 eggs, beaten
1 cup Parmesan cheese
2 crushed garlic cloves
1 package frozen spinach
    (cooked and drained)
2 cups sliced mushrooms
salt and pepper to taste

Mix together all ingredients except chicken breasts, and season with salt and pepper. Put some of the mixture in each chicken breast and roll. Bake at 350° for 1 hour. Serves 4.

...this is a rich entree and would probably go best with more bland side dishes.

Marti Erickson – Honolulu, Hawaii

lemon chicken

1 pound boned chicken
2 tablespoons soy sauce
1 tablespoon sherry
1 clove garlic, minced
1 teaspoon minced ginger
1 teaspoon sugar
1 egg white
2 teaspoons cornstarch
1 teaspoon flour
1/2 lemon, thinly sliced
oil for deep frying

lemon sauce

1/2 cup chicken broth
1/3 cup sugar
2 tablespoons vinegar
juice of 1-1/2 lemons
2 teaspoons cornstarch
1 tablespoon water
2 drops yellow food coloring

Pound the chicken lightly with the back of a knife blade. Cut chicken into pieces, 1-1/2 inches by 1 inch. Combine soy sauce, sherry, garlic, ginger and sugar. Add to chicken. Marinate for 30 minutes. Heat oil in a wok to 375°. Drain chicken. Combine egg white, cornstarch and flour. Coat each piece of chicken. Fry until golden brown. Set aside and keep warm. Prepare lemon sauce. Place chicken on platter. Top with lemon slices and pour lemon sauce over chicken.

For sauce: in a wok, combine broth, sugar, vinegar and lemon juice. Bring to a boil. Mix together cornstarch and water. Stir into broth mixture. Reduce heat and cook until thickened and clear. Remove from heat and stir in food coloring.

Barbara Gray – Honolulu, Hawaii

celestial honeymoon chicken

Arrange a large chicken breast, boned and halved, in a shallow pan dotted with 1 tablespoon butter.

In a saucepan, combine 1/3 cup apricot preserves, 1-1/2 tablespoons lemon juice and 1 teaspoon lemon pepper to make a marinade. Blend well. Heat until preserves melt. Pour sauce over chicken and sprinkle slivered almonds on top. Bake uncovered at 350° for 40-45 minutes, basting occasionally.

…this recipe is easy to double or triple.

Beth Davison – Oklahoma City, Oklahoma

maple syrup chicken

12 chicken thighs

marinade

1 cup maple syrup
1 tablespoon salad oil
2 ounces wine vinegar
1 tablespoon soy sauce
1-3/4 cups tomato sauce
2 tablespoons curry powder
1 tablespoon marjoram
4 cloves, crushed
salt and pepper
1/2 cup dry sherry

2 stalks celery, chopped
2 cups mushrooms, sliced
1 large onion, chopped
2 ounces raisins

Combine ingredients of marinade and pour over chicken. Let sit for 4 hours. Then put chicken and marinade into a pot and bring to a boil. Simmer for 30 minutes.

Add to the pot the celery, mushrooms, onion, and raisins and simmer 30 minutes more. Serves 6-8.

Patti Spengler – Honolulu, Hawaii

baked chicken with kumquats

1 roasting chicken, about 4 pounds
1/2 cup dry white wine
1/4 cup lime juice
1/4 cup soy sauce
1 cup finely chopped onions
4 cloves garlic, crushed
1/2 teaspoon oregano
1/2 teaspoon thyme
1 teaspoon curry powder
1 teaspoon ground ginger
2 tablespoons butter
1 tablespoon salad oil
3 tablespoons flour
1 cup canned or bottled kumquats, cut
    in half, do not use fresh kumquats
3/4 cup reserved kumquat liquid
2 egg yolks, lightly beaten

Cut chicken into serving pieces and place in a large, shallow bowl. Combine the next 9 ingredients and pour over chicken. Cover and allow to marinate about 8 hours, turning twice. Drain chicken and reserve marinade.

Heat butter and oil in a large frying pan. Brown chicken and return to baking dish. Stir flour into the fat remaining in the pan and cook, stirring until bubbly. Gradually stir in marinade and cook until thickened. Pour sauce over chicken and cover dish with foil. Place in a preheated oven at 350° for 1 hour, or until tender.

Remove chicken from sauce and place in a shallow serving dish. Arrange kumquats around chicken and keep warm.

Pour sauce from baking dish into a small saucepan. Bring to a boil. Blend some of the hot liquid with the egg yolks, then return mixture to pan. Add kumquat syrup. Cook, stirring constantly, until sauce is thickened. Do not boil. Add salt to taste and pour over chicken. Serves 6.

Susan Nicholson – Honolulu, Hawaii

hawaiian baked chicken

1/2 cup oil
1 cup flour
1 teaspoon seasoned salt
4 pounds chicken pieces
1 cup orange juice
2 tablespoons lemon juice
1/2 cup brown sugar
1 tablespoon cornstarch
1 tablespoon soy sauce
1/2 teaspoon salt
2 cups sliced papaya

Pour oil into large pan. Combine flour and seasoned salt. Remove skin from chicken and dredge pieces in flour mixture. Arrange in baking pan. Bake at 350° for 40 minutes. Turn and bake 20 minutes longer.

In a saucepan, combine remaining ingredients except papaya and cook until thickened. Gently stir in papaya and pour mixture over chicken. Bake 10 minutes longer. (Makes 10 14-ounce servings of protein).

Jo Starr – Honolulu, Hawaii

polynesian chicken

6 whole chicken breasts
salt and pepper
flour
1 small can frozen orange juice
1 small can frozen pineapple juice
1/3 cup white wine
oil for frying
1 package slivered almonds, toasted

Bone chicken breasts and cut in half. Season with salt and pepper and dredge in flour. In a bowl, combine orange and pineapple juice and white wine.

Brown chicken in oil and transfer to shallow casserole. Pour juice and wine mixture over chicken and bake at 375° for 20-25 minutes or until done. Baste chicken several times during baking. About 5 minutes before chicken is done, scatter almonds over chicken and baste. Watch carefully that almonds do not burn.

...if you can't find frozen pineapple juice, substitute regular pineapple juice.

Dorothy McMillan – Honolulu, Hawaii

my chicken recipe

1 3-1/2-pound fryer chicken
1 stick butter
2 egg yolks
1 cup bread crumbs
salt and white pepper

Cut chicken into pieces and remove skin. Sprinkle with salt and pepper. Melt 1/2 stick of butter and reserve in pan to keep melted. Slightly beat egg yolks.

Have the melted butter, egg yolks and bread crumbs in separate bowls near the stove. Have the remaining 1/2 stick of butter melting at medium high temperature. First dip the chicken pieces in the butter, then egg yolk and then roll in bread crumbs. Place the chicken in the pan with melting butter and brown. Transfer pieces to baking dish and bake at 375° for 30 minutes or until tender.

Amie Bowlen – Honolulu, Hawaii
Sally's daughter

chicken parmesan

1-1/2 cups Italian bread crumbs
1/2 cup fresh Parmesan cheese
1 teaspoon salt
1 teaspoon pepper
6 chicken breasts, boned and skinned
1/4 pound butter

Combine bread crumbs, cheese, salt and pepper. Dip chicken in melted butter, then in bread crumbs, being sure to coat each piece heavily.
Place chicken in a baking dish and bake at 350° for 30-35 minutes, uncovered. Do not turn chicken.

…this freezes very well before or after baking…to reheat after thawing, bake at 355° until hot…it is very good served with a savory rice dish.

Claire Smith – Dallas, Texas

plantation baked stuffed chicken

6 to 8 chicken breasts
2 pounds ricotta cheese
1 cup whole wheat bread crumbs
1-1/2 pounds zucchini
2 teaspoons basil
4 scallions, including greens
1/2 cup grated Parmesan cheese
2 eggs
salt and pepper
1 teaspoon each – rosemary,
    marjoram and thyme
1 teaspoon oil

Lay chicken breasts out flat with skin and bone remaining. Very carefully, separate the skin from the chicken, being certain not to tear the skin. Rub salt and pepper over chicken under the skin and on the underside (place the chicken breasts skin side up when cooking). Sieve (make into crumbs) the ricotta cheese in a processor. Grate the zucchini. Squeeze it dry and put through a food processor. Add the bread crumbs, zucchini, chopped scallions, basil and Parmesan cheese. Season with salt and pepper. Add beaten eggs and mix well. Stuff the mixture between the skin and the flesh of the chicken breasts. Put as much stuffing as possible. (Stuffing is low in calories). Then secure skin to meat with toothpicks. Rub the outside of the chicken with safflower oil or olive oil and then rub lightly with the herb mixture, which you combine with a little salt and pepper. Smear this over the servings. Bake the chicken breasts at 325° for 1-1/2 hours or until chicken is done. Cover with aluminum foil while baking. Remove toothpicks before serving.

…this recipe is considered to be American Nouvelle Cuisine.

Katherine Levitz – Ft. Lauderdale, Florida

beefed up chicken

4 chicken breasts, boned and skinned
4 slices bacon
3 ounce package diced corned beef
1 can mushroom soup
1 cup sour cream

Wrap each chicken breast in bacon slice. Place 2 thin slices dried corned beef on top and place in baking dish. Mix mushroom soup (undiluted) with sour cream and pour over chicken. Bake at 275° for 3 hours.

Beth Wright – Oklahoma City, Oklahoma

poulet dijon

2 chickens, about 3 pounds each,
      quartered
salt and pepper
1/4 cup butter
2 tablespoons Dijon mustard
1 clove garlic, chopped
1 small onion, chopped
1 10-1/2-ounce can condensed
      chicken broth
1 tablespoon flour
2 tablespoons parsley, finely chopped

Sprinkle chicken on all sides with salt and pepper. In a large skillet, heat butter and brown the chicken pieces slowly on all sides. In a small bowl, mix remaining ingredients until well blended. Pour mixture over chicken. Simmer, turning pieces occasionally until chicken is tender, about 40 minutes. Remove chicken to platter. Stir pan juices, scraping all brown particles from pan. Simmer until sauce is slightly thickened. Spoon sauce over chicken. Serve with hot petits pois, and champignons de Paris, which are button mushrooms. Makes about 8 servings.

Jane Morris – Ponca City, Oklahoma

harold's tipsey chicken

2 fryers, cut up and cleaned

basting sauce for charcoaled chicken

1/4 cup butter
juice of 1/2 lemon
1/2 teaspoon paprika
1/3 cup Cointreau
1/4 cup olive oil
1/2 teaspoon Tabasco sauce
1/2 teaspoon seasoned salt

Heat all ingredients in a small pan. As a suggestion, flavor of chicken greatly depends on being charcoaled rather than grilled on Jennaire or outdoor gas grill. Grill chicken 35 to 40 minutes. Baste frequently.

sauce

1 can Oregon gooseberries, drained
1/2 cup sugar
1 teaspoon grated lemon rind
6 ounces red currant jelly
2 whole cloves
2 tablespoons Cointreau

Mix all ingredients, bring to a boil until sugar melts. Set aside. Serve in a sauce boat, after spooning a little sauce over each piece of chicken.

This original recipe is an award winning one from a mutual friend, Harold Taylor, Ponca City, Oklahoma.

Coni Osborn – Lubbock, Texas

"sunday" fried chicken fricassee

1 chicken cut into pieces – rubbed with salt, pepper, and paprika. Roll pieces in flour and shake off surplus flour.

Drop into a large dutch oven pot with hot oil or Crisco. Brown to a golden color and remove pieces. Remove oil from dutch oven. Put chicken back and add hot water to cover. Add diced celery, a small chopped onion, crushed garlic and chopped parsley. Cook until tender, gravy will be thin. Blend 1 or 2 tablespoons flour with 1 tablespoon melted butter and add to gravy. Add a little Kitchen Bouquet for darkening gravy to a nice brown color.

Use your leftover "Sunday" fried chicken with this recipe. It is perfect.

Margaret Katz Goldman (Mrs. S.N. Goldman)
– Oklahoma City, Oklahoma

chicken lasagne

8 ounces noodles
2 cans mushroom soup
1 cup milk
3/4 teaspoon salt
1/3 chopped green pepper
4 cups cubed chicken meat
1/2 teaspoon poultry seasoning
1 8-ounce package cream cheese
1-1/2 cups cottage cheese
1/2 cup chopped onion
1/4 cup minced parsley
1-1/2 cups bread crumbs, buttered
    and salted

Cook noodles; drain and rinse. Beat cheeses, milk, soup and seasonings together. Layer noodles, then chicken and then soup mixture in casserole. Repeat with remaining 1/2 of ingredients. Bake at 375° for 1 hour. Let stand a few minutes before serving.

…use bread crumbs only on top layer.

…this is better if refrigerated overnight before baking.

Brenda Dutton Lennox – Calgary, Alberta, Canada

chicken casserole

2 tablespoons grated onion
1 cup cooked chicken
1 cup cooked celery
1 cup cooked rice
1 cup chicken soup
3/4 cup mayonnaise
1 can water chestnuts, sliced
1/2 cup slivered almonds

Cook celery only briefly so it remains crisp. For added flavor, cook celery and rice in chicken broth instead of water. Combine all ingredients and place in a buttered baking dish. Bake 45 minutes at 350°.

You may add a topping by melting 1/4 pound margarine and adding 1 cup crushed corn flakes. Spread on casserole just before serving, or last few minutes of baking time.

Norma Owens – Honolulu, Hawaii

honey barbecued chicken

1 2-1/2 to 3-pound frying chicken,
    cut up
1 egg yolk
1/8 teaspoon pepper
1/4 teaspoon salt
1/2 teaspoon paprika
2 tablespoons soy sauce
2 tablespoons lemon juice
1/4 cup honey
2 tablespoons butter, melted

Wash chicken pieces and pat dry with paper towel. Beat egg yolk slightly, then blend remaining ingredients in a bowl.

Dip chicken pieces into sauce and place in a 9 x 12 x 2-inch baking pan. Pour remaining sauce over chicken. Bake uncovered for 30 minutes at 400°. Turn chicken, baste with sauce in pan. Continue baking at 400° for 35 to 40 minutes, until chicken is tender.

A bottle of chilled good wine adds the gourmet touch!

This sauce is wonderful on the barbecue…baste frequently when barbecuing.

Wallace Edwards – Ponca City, Oklahoma

chicken-broccoli casserole

2 10-ounce packages frozen broccoli
2 cups cooked diced chicken
2 cans cream of mushroom soup
1 cup mayonnaise
1/2 teaspoon curry powder
1 teaspoon lemon juice
1/2 cup grated sharp cheese
1/2 cup bread crumbs

Cook broccoli and drain. Place in the bottom of an 8 x 13-inch casserole. Cover with chicken. Mix soup, mayonnaise, curry and lemon juice. Spread over chicken. Top with grated cheese and bread crumbs. Bake, uncovered at 350° for 20 to 30 minutes.

Jayne Black – Aspen, Colorado

italian chicken casserole

2 6-ounce jars artichoke hearts
4 tablespoons olive oil
1/4 cup flour
2 pounds boneless chicken breasts
    and thighs
6 tomatoes (or canned tomatoes), drained
4 small cloves garlic
1 pound fresh mushrooms
1 cup dry sherry
2 tablespoons fresh parsley
1-1/2 teaspoons salt
3/4 teaspoon pepper
2 teaspoons dried basil
1 teaspoon monosodium glutamate
1 teaspoon dried oregano
parsley sprigs for garnish

Drain artichokes and save liquid for later. Combine 1/2 of the artichoke liquid with oil in 10 or 12-inch skillet. Heat over low heat. Place flour in a paper bag and place pieces of chicken inside. Shake to coat pieces thoroughly. Brown chicken for 5 to 7 minutes on each side over medium high heat. Transfer chicken to a 3-quart casserole. Peel and quarter tomatoes. Combine with sherry, salt, pepper, oregano, msg, basil, minced garlic, sliced mushrooms and minced fresh parsley. Place in a skillet and simmer over low heat for 10 minutes. Pour sauce over chicken. Bake uncovered at 350° for 50 minutes. Add artichokes and refrigerate overnight. Cover casserole and heat 25 minutes at 350° before serving.

Serve with rice or vermicelli. Garnish with parsley.

Jeannine Davi – Honolulu, Hawaii

chicken rice casserole

1 chicken
1 can cream of mushroom soup
1 can cream of celery soup
1 package dried onion soup mix
1 soup can of water
8 ounces slow cooking rice

Cut chicken into pieces and sprinkle lightly with salt and pepper. Mix the soups with water. In a pyrex baking dish, layer the rice, then the chicken, and cover with the soup mixture. Cover the dish with foil. Bake at 350° for 2 hours, removing the foil the last half hour so chicken will brown.

Pat Drake – Ponca City, Oklahoma

french bread filled with chicken

8 whole chicken breasts, boned
4 green peppers
2 red sweet peppers
4 tomatoes
6 cloves garlic, chopped
1/2 cup parsley, chopped
1 cup olive oil
3 tablespoons Dijon mustard
1 teaspoon basil
1 teaspoon oregano
3 to 4 tablespoons lemon juice or vinegar

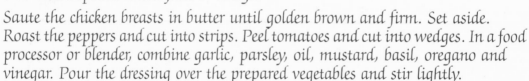

Saute the chicken breasts in butter until golden brown and firm. Set aside. Roast the peppers and cut into strips. Peel tomatoes and cut into wedges. In a food processor or blender, combine garlic, parsley, oil, mustard, basil, oregano and vinegar. Pour the dressing over the prepared vegetables and stir lightly.

Cut the french bread from one end to another. Place the chicken breasts along the loaf and cover with the vegetable mixture. Cut into 8 serving pieces per loaf and place on a large platter with lettuce liner. Serves 16.

Lavonne Tollerud – Honolulu, Hawaii

easy overnight turkey

1 20-pound hen turkey
1/2 stick butter
1 large clove garlic, slivered
1 large peeled onion, quartered
1 large unpeeled apple, quartered

Rinse turkey and wipe dry. Rub inside and out with half the butter. Place remaining butter inside cavity. Place garlic, onion and apple in cavity. Do not salt or pepper the bird. Place breast-side down on rack in roaster. Bake for 1 hour at 325°. Turn bird on back and reduce heat to 200°. Bake, uncovered, without opening oven, for 10 to 12 hours. Serves 12.

Sugar and Spice

southern stuffing for turkey

5 cups soft bread crumbs
5 cups crumbled corn bread
1/2 cup butter, melted
1 cup chopped pecans
3/4 cup finely chopped onions
1/2 cup finely chopped celery
1 cup chicken stock, or use
    1 bouillon cube
1 cup water
1/2 cup pork sausage meat
1/2 teaspoon salt
1/4 teaspoon pepper
1/2 teaspoon thyme
1/2 teaspoon marjoram
1/4 teaspoon basil
2 eggs, beaten

Combine all ingredients and mix well. Bake at 325° until at serving consistency, about 1 hour.

Sugar and Spice

chicken livers with cumin

1-1/4 pounds chicken livers, halved
1 tablespoon salad oil
2 tablespoons butter
1 medium sized onion, finely chopped
1 medium sized clove garlic, very finely minced
2 teaspoons cumin
3 tablespoons cognac
1 16-ounce can plum tomatoes, coarsely chopped
2 teaspoons beef extract
1 tablespoon finely minced parsley
salt, pepper and cayenne pepper to taste

Wash livers and drain well. Heat oil and butter in saucepan over moderate heat. Saute livers until browned. Add onion, garlic and cumin, mixing well, and saute for 3 more minutes. Add cognac; set aflame.

Let flame burn out. Add tomatoes, beef extract and parsley. Season generously and simmer for 5 minutes. Keep warm in chafing dish. Serves 6.

Sugar and Spice

roast wild duck à la teal club

The key to cooking wild duck properly is simplicity…a very hot oven for a relatively short time. Stuffing with celery, onion, apple, etc. is not only unnecessary, but steams the bird's cavity rather than letting it roast.

Preheat the oven to 500° Rub the bird lightly with olive oil and salt it quite liberally. The length of roasting time is obviously dependent on the size of the bird.

The following timetable seems to work quite well:
    mallard…25 minutes
    sprig (pintail)…22 minutes
    teal…15 minutes

Wild rice and glazed carrots complement duck nicely. Heating plum jam with some port added makes a delicious sauce.

…I prefer a good Zinfandel with duck.

Stephen R. Arelt – Mill Valley, California

Chervil

chervil

Mediterranean origin...Pliny of Rome
recommended doses of vinegar soaked with
chervil seeds as a remedy for hiccoughs
...later it gained religious significance
and was symbolically eaten during Lent
since it was thought to be a blood purifier.

Pork & Lamb

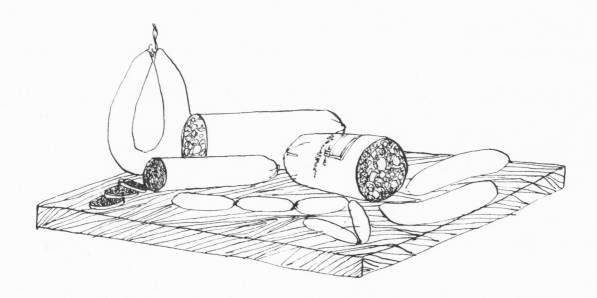

pork paprika

3 pounds pork loin or chops
1 tablespoon flour
1 teaspoon paprika per serving
2 cups good beef stock
1 medium onion
2 tablespoons butter
1 cup sour cream (at room temperature)

Sprinkle pork with a little paprika and set aside. Chop onion fine and saute in butter until clear. Add pork loin or chops. Brown on all sides but do not cook through. (It is important not to overcook at this stage). Remove meat from pan onto heated dish, leaving remaining onion and juices in pan. Add all the paprika and flour to pan and cook for about 5 minutes...be sure not to burn it. Add cold beef stock all at once and bring to a boil. Cook to reduce to about 1-1/2 cups. Taste at this stage then add salt and pepper to taste. Remove from heat and add sour cream all at once. (If the sauce is boiling, the cream will separate). When all the cream is incorporated, put the pork back into the sauce and reheat to serving temperature. This dish can also be kept warm in the oven, but do not let it boil. Serve with spaetzle. Serves 6.

Wolf H. Lehmkuhl – Honolulu, Hawaii

filet of pork with tarragon sauce

2 pounds of pork filet
2 teaspoons dried tarragon
3 tablespoons butter
2 tablespoons oil
1/4 cup white tarragon vinegar
3/4 cup beef stock
1/2 tablespoon Dijon mustard
3 teaspoons fresh tarragon
3/4 to 1 cup heavy cream
salt and freshly ground pepper

Cut the pork into 1-inch slices and place them between two sheets of wax paper. Flatten them with a meat pounder. Season both sides of the meat with tarragon, salt and pepper.

Heat the oil and butter in a skillet until the butter stops foaming. Saute the meat slices over medium-high heat until brown on both sides. Transfer to an oven-proof serving platter. When meat is browning, it is important not to let the pieces touch each other as that releases the juices. When all the meat has been sauteed, pour off any excess fat, and deglaze the pan with vinegar, scraping up any brown bits. Let the vinegar reduce somewhat before adding the beef broth. Simmer for a couple of minutes, scraping up any meat glaze on the bottom of the pan.

Add 3 teaspoons tarragon, mustard and the cream. The cream should be added little by little until the sauce is thickened. Adjust seasoning and pour over meat. Preheat oven to 350°.

30 minutes before serving, heat in oven.

...veal scallopini can be used insead of pork.

Jennifer Loving – New York, New York

royal pork chops

6 pork chops
6 tablespoons rice
6 tomato slices
6 green pepper slices
6 onion slices, each about 1/2 inch
6 slices Cheddar cheese
1 can cream of mushroom soup,
    with enough water added to make
    2 cups liquid
1 8-ounce can tomato sauce

Brown pork chops on each side and arrange in a single layer in a 13 x 9-inch baking dish. Season with salt and pepper. On each chop, place in this order: 1 tablespoon rice, 1 tomato slice, 1 green pepper slice, 1 onion slice.

Mix soup with water and tomato sauce. Carefully pour over chops. Cover baking dish and bake at 350° for 1 to 1-1/2 hours or until rice is tender. Remove onion slice carefully and place cheese slice on top of pepper. Replace onion on top of cheese and bake an additional 10 minutes.

Connie Baldwin – Honolulu, Hawaii

pork chops florentine

6 rib or loin pork chops
2 tablespoons warm cognac
2 tablespoons olive oil
2 teaspoons salt
1/4 teaspoon freshly ground black pepper
3 tablespoons butter
3 tablespoons flour
1 cup milk
1/2 cup grated cheddar cheese
2 packages frozen spinach,
    cooked and drained
1/2 teaspoon Dijon mustard

Cut chops 3/4 to 1-inch thick. Preheat oven to 350°. Brown chops in oil and pour off drippings. Pour warm cognac over chops, stand back and ignite. When flame subsides, season chops with 1-1/2 teaspoons of the salt and 1/8 teaspoon of the pepper.

Melt butter, blend in flour and gradually stir in the milk. Bring to a boil, stirring constantly. Add remaining salt and pepper, the cheese, spinach and mustard. Blend well.

Pour into a greased, shallow baking dish and arrange pork chops over the top. Cover and bake for 30 minutes. Remove cover and continue baking 15 minutes or until chops are well cooked. Serves 6.

Janet Schiller – Honolulu, Hawaii

my "ham loaf"

2 pounds ham
1-1/2 pounds pork
1-1/4 cups cracker crumbs
3 eggs
1 can tomato soup
1 cup milk
dash of Tabasco
1 tablespoon Worcestershire sauce

sauce

1/2 cup brown sugar
1/4 cup vinegar
1 tablespoon mustard
1/4 teaspoon cloves

Have the ham and pork ground together at the market. Place the meat in a large bowl and add the cracker crumbs, eggs, tomato soup, milk, Tabasco and Worcestershire sauces. Mix thoroughly with hands and place in a baking dish 12 x 14 inches. Baste with the sauce.

For sauce, mix brown sugar, vinegar, mustard and cloves. Bring to a boil and pour over meat.

Bake at 350° for 1-1/2 hours. Serves 15.

Dorothy Paynter Crawford – Ponca City, Oklahoma

butterflied leg of lamb

1 large leg of lamb
1 large bottle Wishbone Italian dressing
1 large onion, grated
1/2 teaspoon thyme
1-1/2 teaspoons garlic powder
4 ounces mint jelly
1/2 cup dry white wine

Have your butcher bone and butterfly the lamb for you. Combine other ingredients to make a marinade and pour over the lamb. Marinate at least 6 hours or preferably overnight. Turn the meat over every so often. Charcoal grill as you would a steak, approximately 15 to 20 minutes each side. Baste with marinade.

Cynnie Bell Ayau – Honolulu, Hawaii

stuffed lamb chops

4 large lamb chops, 1-1/2 inches thick
3 tablespoons butter
2 tablespoons onion chopped
1/2 cup mushrooms, chopped
2 tablespoons bread crumbs
2 tablespoons goose liver paté
3 tablespoons stock or bouillon
Worcestershire sauce, salt and pepper
      to taste

Split chops and broil on one side. Press open and stuff.

To make stuffing, brown all ingredients in butter.

After stuffing, broil chops on opposite side and serve.

Evelyn Pfifer – Honolulu, Hawaii

lamb curry

4 pounds lamb (fat free)
6 medium onions
enough oil to brown onions
3/4 tablespoon powdered turmeric
1-1/2 tablespoons coriander powder
1/2 tablespoon cumin powder
3/4 tablespoon fresh ginger
1/4 teaspoon cayenne pepper
1 cup plain yogurt
3 ripe, fresh tomatoes or
      canned, drained tomatoes

Cut lamb in 2-inch pieces. Chop onions fine and brown in oil. Add lamb, turmeric, coriander, cumin, finely chopped ginger and fry for 10-12 minutes. Add yogurt, chopped tomatoes, salt and cayenne. Keep stirring occasionally and cook until meat is tender. Serve with hot rice and mango chutney.

Indru Watumull – Honolulu, Hawaii

oregano

oregano

Mediterranean origin...sharper and stronger tasting than its relative marjoram, it grows wild in many places and became popular in America as an ingredient in ethnic cuisine...most notably, it is associated with Italian foods as an additive to pastas and sauces.

Rice & Pasta

wild rice connors

2 cups wild rice
1 can consommé
3/4 cup celery
3/4 cup green pepper
1 medium onion
1 cup sliced mushrooms, sauteed
1 stick butter
salt and pepper

Wash wild rice thoroughly and soak overnight. Boil rice in consommé until tender, about 20 or 30 minutes. You may have to add more consommé. Dice celery, chop green pepper and onion, and saute in butter. Combine all ingredients in casserole and bake slowly at 300° for 1/2 hour or until heated thoroughly. Serves 8-10.

Shirley Connors – Honolulu, Hawaii

rizotto a la milanaise

1 cup long grain rice (Uncle Ben's)
2 ounces butter
1 tablespoon chopped onions
1 clove garlic, chopped fine
3 cups chicken bouillon
2 ounces tomato sauce
2 ounces grated Parmesan cheese
salt and pepper to taste

Saute the onions and garlic in butter (do not brown). Then add the rice, chicken bouillon, tomato sauce and salt and pepper to taste. Bring to a boil and bake in the oven for 20 minutes at 325°. Remove from the oven and add the Parmesan cheese. Mix well and serve.

George Mendreshora – Honolulu, Hawaii

gourmet rice

1 tablespoon butter
1 small onion
2 bunches lettuce leaves
1/3 cup sliced mushrooms
1 large tomato
3/4 cup white rice
1 pimento
1-1/2 cups hot chicken broth
3/4 teaspoon salt
dash of pepper
2 tablespoons slivered toasted almonds
2 tablespoons sauteed raisins
paprika

Melt butter in saucepan and add finely chopped onions. Cook until soft but not brown. Add shredded lettuce, mushrooms, rice and tomato, peeled, seeded and chopped. Mix well and add broth, salt and pepper. Bring to a boil. Cover and cook on low heat for 20 minutes. Remove from heat and toss with a fork. Add diced pimento and raisins. Toss again and serve with paprika and almonds.

Sugar and Spice

texas monterey cheese rice

1 cup uncooked rice
2 cups sour cream
1 can Ortega chopped green chiles
1 pound Monterey Jack cheese, grated
butter

Cook rice. Combine with sour cream and season with salt. Arrange half of the mixture in a buttered, 2-quart casserole. Layer with Jack cheese and chopped green chiles. Top with remaining rice mixture. Sprinkle top with grated cheese and dot with butter. Bake at 325° for 30 minutes.

…this may be frozen, then thawed 1 hour and then baked.

Helen L Frost – Wichita Falls, Texas

noodle pudding

1 10-ounce package medium noodles
4 eggs, well beaten
1 pint sour cream
1 16-ounce container cottage cheese,
    small curd
1/4 cup sugar
1 teaspoon vanilla
3/4 cup milk
dash of cinnamon
1/2 cup white raisins
1 stick melted butter
corn flakes
brown sugar (1/4 cup approx.)

Cook noodles in salted water. Drain. Mix all ingredients except corn flakes and brown sugar. Put in a flat baking dish. Sprinkle crushed corn flakes on top and cover with brown sugar. Bake at 350° for 1 hour.

…noodle puddings go well with lots of dishes. This one has been in my family for years and is always included in any family parties.

Dale Hower Solheim – Aspen, Colorado

zucchini with linguine

1/2 cup onion
2 tablespoons shallots
3 tablespoons butter
3 tablespoons olive oil
1/2 cup diced prosciutto
freshly ground pepper to taste
2 pounds zucchini
1 pound linguine
freshly ground Parmesan

Melt butter in a skillet. Chop onion, mince shallots and add to the melted butter and oil. Cook until transparent, stirring to cook evenly. Slice the zucchini into rounds, the rounds into quarters and add. Cook, stirring from 2 to 3 minutes. Add the prosciutto and pepper.

Cook the linguine in boiling water until cooked but al dente. Drain, and put in a heated bowl. Toss all ingredients together. Pass the grated Parmesan.

…zucchini should be firm and slender when you buy it.

Angela Mancinelli – Honolulu, Hawaii

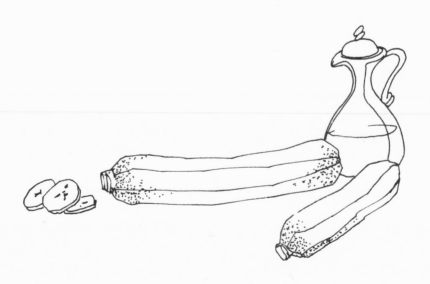

linguine à la filomena

2 tablespoons olive oil
2 garlic cloves
1/4 teaspoon crushed red pepper
1/2 pound linguine
salt

Fill a large pot with water and start to boil for pasta. Heat olive oil in a large skillet and push garlic through a press into oil. Add crushed red pepper and cook for a few minutes. Add linguine and 1/2 tablespoon salt to rapidly boiling water. Cook pasta till al dente. Drain and turn into oil and garlic mixture. Toss to coat pasta well and sprinkle with grated Parmesan cheese. Serve immediately. Serves 4.

Filomena Buck – Honolulu, Hawaii

cheese manicotti

1 package (of 10) manicotti noodles
6 ounces Parmesan cheese, grated
6 ounces Romano cheese, grated
2 eggs, beaten
1-1/2 cups chopped black olives
1 cup cottage cheese
1 cup grated Muenster cheese
1 cup grated Monterey Jack cheese
2 teaspoons oregano
1 teaspoon pepper
2 8-ounce cans tomato sauce

Boil manicotti noodles. Mix together grated cheese and remaining ingredients except tomato sauce. Slit each manicotti noodle and fill with mixture. Layer the bottom of a casserole dish with 1 can of tomato sauce. Place stuffed manicotti in casserole dish. Cover top of noodles with remaining can of tomato sauce. Bake at 350° for 1/2 hour. Let stand for 10 minutes before serving. Serves 4.

Marti Erickson – Honolulu, Hawaii

lasagne pesto swirls

8 lasagne noodles
1 cup freshly grated Parmesan cheese
1-1/3 cups ricotta cheese
1/2 teaspoon each, salt and pepper
1/4 teaspoon ground nutmeg
1   10-ounce package frozen, chopped
    spinach

pesto sauce

2 cloves garlic, minced
2 cups tightly packed fresh basil leaves
1/4 cup freshly grated Parmesan cheese
2 tablespoons pinenuts or walnuts
1/2 to 2/3 cup olive oil
1/4 cup fresh parsley

Cook lasagne. Drain and set aside. Spinach should be thawed and moisture squeezed out. Mix together spinach, 3/4 cup Parmesan, ricotta, salt, pepper and nutmeg. Spread about 1/2 cup cheese mixture along entire length of each noodle. Then roll noodles up and stand on end in a greased casserole dish, 2-1/2 inches deep.

For sauce, combine ingredients in a food processor, adding enough olive oil to make a smooth sauce. Pour sauce over each noodle. If sauce is too thick, add more oil.

Bake, covered in a 350° oven for about 30 minutes. Remove and sprinkle with remaining 1/4 cup Parmesan. Serves 4 large or 8 small servings.

Devon Guard – Honolulu, Hawaii

mock ravioli

meat sauce layers

1 large clove garlic
2 medium onions, chopped
3 tablespoons salad oil
2 pounds ground chuck
1 can tomato sauce
1 can tomato paste
1 to 1-1/2 cups water
3/4 teaspoon each, oregano, rosemary
2 cups mushrooms, sliced

Brown onions, minced garlic, and meat in salad oil. Stir in the mushrooms with the remaining ingredients and simmer for 2 hours.

spinach layers

1 cup salad oil
4 packages chopped, frozen spinach
1 cup parsley, chopped
2 cups soft bread crumbs
1 cup Parmesan cheese
1 teaspoon ground sage
1 teaspoon garlic salt
6 eggs, well beaten

Combine all ingredients and mix well.

pasta layer

1 pound butterfly macaroni, cooked and drained well. Sprinkle chopped parsley and Parmesan cheese over the cooked macaroni and mix well.

Butter a large baking dish and cover the bottom with a layer of macaroni, then a layer of spinach mixture and last, a layer of the meat sauce. Repeat this until all the ingredients are used, ending with the meat sauce. Sprinkle top with Parmesan cheese and parsley. Bake at 350° for 30-40 minutes. Serves 10-12.

…this can be prepared ahead and frozen.

Patti Spengler – Honolulu, Hawaii

spaetzle

2 cups flour
1/2 teaspoon nutmeg
ground pepper
1 teaspoon salt
2 eggs, beaten
milk
1-1/2 sticks butter
bread crumbs (optional)

Mix flour, nutmeg, pepper and salt together. Add eggs and enough milk
to make a stiff batter. Let stand for an hour. Boil salted water in a large
saucepan. Pour the batter through a spaetzle sieve. The spaetzle will come
to the surface when cooked…about 4 minutes. Drain and run water through
as you would for pasta. This dish can be made in advance to this stage.
Ten minutes before serving, saute the spaetzle in 1-1/2 sticks butter (hot),
add more salt and pepper to taste and fine bread crumbs may also be
added. Spaetzle should be golden in color. Serves 6.

Wolf H. Lehmkuhl – Honolulu, Hawaii

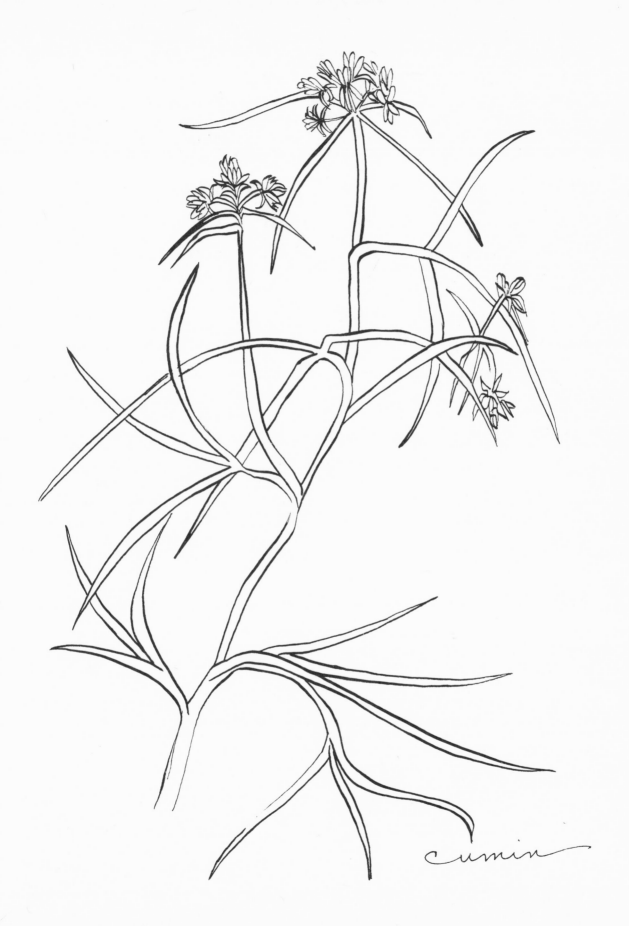

cumin

cumin

Middle eastern origin...its recorded use dates from pre-Biblical eras like many other herbs, and it too has its place among superstitions and legends...cumin was among the special spices used for tithe payment as well as an ingredient in cakes and bread to compensate for meat during meatless ceremonial fasts in Biblical times.

Vegetables

green bean casserole

3 tablespoons butter
1 can mushroom soup
1 small jar pimentos
1 large green pepper
1/2 pound Old English cheese
3 to 4 cans whole green beans, drained
Ritz crackers

Mix together over medium low heat, butter, soup, chopped pimento, chopped green pepper, and cheese until cheese has melted. Pour over green beans and crumble Ritz crackers on top. Bake at 350° for 40 minutes.

Jacque Monsour – Ponca City, Oklahoma

broccoli mushroom layers

1-1/2 pounds broccoli
3 ounces Parmesan cheese, grated
8 ounces Monterey Jack cheese, grated
3 scallions, thinly sliced
8 ounces fresh mushrooms, thinly sliced
4 eggs
1/4 cup skim milk
1/2 teaspoon dry leaf thyme
1/2 teaspoon dry leaf basil
1/4 teaspoon salt
1 tablespoon unsalted butter

Have Parmesan cheese at room temperature and keep Jack cheese well chilled. Clean and trim broccoli. Steam until crisp, then remove from heat. Saute onions for 30 seconds in unsalted butter, add mushrooms and saute a few minutes longer. Remove from heat. Coarsely chop broccoli and place in a large bowl with mushroom mixture. Thoroughly mix eggs, Parmesan cheese, salt, thyme, and basil. Add to broccoli mixture and mix well. Lightly butter an 8 x 8-inch or a rectangular dish. Spread half the vegetable mixture on the bottom of the baking dish. Top with half the Jack cheese. Make a second layer using the remaining vegetable mixture and cheese. Bake, uncovered, for 30 minutes at 375°. Cut into squares to serve. Serves 4 as a main dish, 6 or 8 as a side dish.

Virginia Stringer – Honolulu, Hawaii

west texas baked beans

1 pound can (med.) pork and beans
1 small can chiles
1/2 large onion
1/2 cup brown sugar
2 tablespoons pickle relish
1/4 cup catsup
bacon strips (for top)

Mix together beans, diced chiles, coarsely chopped onion, sugar, relish and catsup. Pour into baking dish and top with bacon. Bake at 250° for 2 hours.

Hank Edwards – Lubbock, Texas

german sprouts

1 10-ounce package frozen
     brussels sprouts
3 slices bacon
2 tablespoons sugar
1 teaspoon salt
2 tablespoons vinegar
2 tablespoons pimento, chopped
1/2 cup cold water
1-1/2 teaspoons cornstarch

Cook brussels sprouts as directed, drain well. In the same saucepan, fry bacon until crisp, drain on paper towel, reserving 2 tablespoons drippings. To reserved drippings, add sugar, salt, vinegar, pimento, and 1/4 cup water. Combine cornstarch with remaining 1/4 cup water. Add this to vinegar mixture in saucepan. Cook over medium heat stirring constantly until thickened and clear. Add brussels sprouts and heat through. Sprinkle with crumbled bacon.

Sugar and Spice

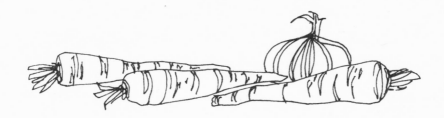

carrot casserole

2 pounds carrots
1 tablespoon onion
1 cup heavy cream
1 teaspoon sugar
salt to taste
4 tablespoons butter
1/2 cup Ritz cracker crumbs

Peel and cook carrots until tender, then mash. Add finely chopped onion, cream, sugar, salt and butter. Put into a greased, two quart casserole and sprinkle crumbs on top. Bake uncovered for 20 to 25 minutes at 325°. Serves 8.

Nancy Kennedy – Honolulu, Hawaii

corn and sour cream with bacon

1 tablespoon onion
1 tablespoon parsley
1/2 pound bacon
2 12-ounce cans whole kernel corn
2 tablespoons butter
1 tablespoon flour
1 teaspoon salt
1 cup sour cream

Chop onion and parsley separately and set aside. Fry bacon until crisp, then crumble. Drain corn. Saute onion in butter until soft. Blend in flour and salt into sauteed onion, then add sour cream gradually, stirring to keep smooth. Heat to boiling point, add corn, heat thoroughly. Add 1/2 cup of bacon and turn into a serving dish. Garnish with remaining bacon and parsley. Serves 8.

Kay Yeary – Ponca City, Oklahoma

danish red cabbage

2-3 pound cabbage
2 cooking apples
1 oz. butter
1/2 cup wine vinegar
1/2 cup water
1/2 cup sugar
1/2 cup red currant jelly

Shred the cabbage and apples. Boil water and vinegar and pour in cabbage. Keep turning the cabbage to even color and cook on a medium heat for 1 hour. Add apples, sugar, butter, currant jelly. Cook again for 1 hour and 15 minutes. Add more sugar if needed.

Red cabbage actually improves if kept for a day before serving and red cabbage can be served at different dinners.

....Preparation time is about 25 minutes and cooking time is 2 hours and 15 minutes. Serves 6.

Osa Nielsen – Honolulu, Hawaii

scalloped corn

1-1/2 cups corn, home cooked or
    canned, whole kernel
1 cup thin cream or evaporated milk
2 tablespoons butter
2 tablespoons flour
1 teaspoon salt
dash of pepper
2 beaten eggs
1/2 cup buttered crumbs

Drain liquid from canned corn into measuring cup; add enough cream or evaporated milk to measure 1 cup. For home cooked corn, use 1 cup cream or evaporated milk.

Heat butter, add flour, salt and pepper. Stir until blended. Slowly add liquid and cook, stirring constantly until thickened. Remove from heat and add drained corn. Slowly add beaten eggs, stirring constantly.

Pour into greased casserole, top with buttered crumbs and sprinkle with paprika. Place in a shallow pan of water. Bake in a moderate oven, 350° for 45 to 50 minutes. Makes 4 to 5 servings.

scalloped corn with clams

before adding eggs, add 1/2 cup fresh or canned clams, drained and finely chopped.

scalloped corn with ham

before adding eggs, add 3/4 cup cooked ground ham or a small can of deviled ham.

scalloped corn with mushrooms

substitute one can of condensed cream of mushroom soup for liquid in making sauce; or saute 1 cup chopped mushrooms in the butter before adding flour and seasonings.

Polly Edwards – Ponca City, Oklahoma

onion corn on the cob

1 envelope dry onion soup mix
    (1-3/8 ounces)
1/2 cup butter or margarine
1/2 teaspoon salt
8 ears of corn

Soften butter or margarine, combine with onion soup mix and salt. Spread each ear of corn with butter mixture, about 1 tablespoon each. Wrap each tightly in foil. Bake at 425° for 30-35 minutes until tender. Serves 8.

....May also be placed on grill over hot coals.

Sugar and Spice

stuffed vegetables à la grecque
dolma filling:

2 pounds ground sirloin
3/4 cup chopped parsley
3/4 cup chopped mint
1 teaspoon fresh dill or
    1/2 teaspoon dried
2 medium onions, chopped
4 scallions
4 tablespoons raw rice
2 teaspoons salt
2 teaspoons pepper
1/4 teaspoon spice parisienne
2 tablespoons water

Vegetables: zucchini, eggplant or peppers, cut in half. Remove some of the center pulp from the zucchini and eggplant. Core and remove the seeds from peppers. Rub the outside with oil.

Mix all the ingredients for the dolma filling lightly but thoroughly with a fork.

Fill vegetables with dolma filling and place in a baking dish. Bake at 375° in a small amount of water or broth, or tomato juice to keep the vegetables from sticking. Bake for approximately 45-60 minutes.

If you don't have spice parisienne you can make it by putting together the 'quatre épices' ... 5 tablespoons ground cloves, 3 tablespoons ground white pepper, 3 teaspoons ground nutmeg, 3 teaspoons ground ginger.

Cleo Evans – Honolulu, Hawaii
The Clever Cooking School

jerry's eggplant parmesan

1 unpeeled eggplant
1 cup oil
1/3 cup bread crumbs
1/3 cup fresh Parmesan cheese
4 tablespoons minced parsley
3 cloves garlic
sliced mozzarella cheese
sliced mushrooms
paprika and pepper

sauce

2 cups fresh tomatoes
almonds
green onions
1/4 cup oil
1 tablespoon tomato paste
1 teaspoon Spike
1 teaspoon pepper
1/2 teaspoon basil
soy sauce
chopped olives

For sauce, peel and chop tomatoes; sliver, toast and chop almonds; chop green onions. Mix together all ingredients and simmer, uncovered, for 1/2 hour, stirring occasionally. Set aside.

Cut unpeeled eggplant into 1/2 inch slices. Season and let stand for 30 minutes so water will come out. Saute eggplant in oil in skillet until browned on both sides. Use medium high heat (add oil 1/2 cup at a time; use more if needed).

Mix bread crumbs, grated Parmesan cheese, 2 tablespoons chopped parsley, minced garlic and dash of pepper in a bowl. Arrange a layer of eggplant in a flat glass dish in one layer. Sprinkle crumb mixture over each. Add tomato mixture on top. Place 1 slice mozzarella cheese over each piece with chopped parsley, paprika, and mushrooms. Bake at 375° for about 20 minutes. Cover top of pan lightly with foil before baking.

Make sure dish is bubbly hot before serving…this dish is frightfully healthy.

….instead of bread crumbs, I use wheat germ.

Jerry Goldman – Los Angeles, California

grandmother's okra

5 slices cooked bacon and drippings
1 large onion, chopped
2 quarts fresh okra, chopped
1 8-ounce can crushed tomatoes
1 medium bell pepper, chopped
salt and pepper to taste

After cooking bacon in a large skillet, saute onion for 3 or 4 minutes. Add remaining ingredients and cook for 45 minutes, covered, on medium-high heat. Stir occasionally and season. Serves 4 to 6. May be put in freezer after cooled... do not salt and pepper if you do so.

Alzada Black – Ponca City, Oklahoma

on the riverside casserole

1 package sharp cheddar cheese, grated
1/4 cup Parmesan cheese
2 tomatoes
1/4 stick butter
6 strips bacon
2 small onions
3 packages frozen okra, or equivalent
    amount fresh
1 8-ounce can tomato sauce
salt and pepper

Grate Parmesan cheese and set aside. Chop tomatoes, onions and bacon separately, and set aside. Place 1/8 of a stick of butter in saucepan and add bacon, onion, salt and pepper to taste. Saute until light brown.

Add another 1/8 stick of butter to bacon mixture, then add okra, tomato sauce, brown sugar and salt and pepper to taste. Cook for 25 minutes, stirring constantly to blend well.

Place in a casserole dish, cover with a layer of cheddar cheese, then sprinkle with Parmesan cheese, and top with bread crumbs.

Bake at 375° to 400° for 10-15 minutes.

Kate Fanish Rivers – Aspen, Colorado

potato ambrosia

1/2 cup Parmesan cheese
1 cup whipping cream, cream or
    canned milk
1/2 tablespoon ground pepper
1/2 stick butter
pulp from 6 potatoes (see baked potato
    skins recipe)

Place pulp from 6 baked potatoes in a 9-inch pyrex dish. Dot with butter.
Sprinkle with ground pepper and Parmesan cheese, on top. Pour whipping
cream, cream or canned milk over potatoes. Cover with Saran Wrap and micro-
wave for 4-5 minutes or bake at 350° for 10-12 minutes.

Sandy Conrad – Maui, Hawaii

baked potato skins

6 large baking potatoes
1/2 cup unsalted butter
fresh ground pepper

optional:

1 cup bacon
8 ounces cheddar cheese

Scrub potatoes and bake at 400° for 1 hour. Melt butter and set aside. When
potatoes are cool enough to handle, halve each one and scoop out the pulp
(reserve pulp for "potato ambrosia" recipe). Cut each potato half lengthwise into
thirds. Place on cookie sheet, brush with butter, and grind fresh pepper over
all. Broil on low rack a few minutes until lightly browned.

For a variation, fry bacon until crisp, then crumble. Grate cheddar cheese, set
both aside separately. After browning potatoes, sprinkle with crumbled bacon and
cheese. Return to oven for a few minutes, until cheese is just melted.

Sandy Conrad – Maui, Hawaii

perfect potato salad

4 cups diced boiled potatoes
1 large, finely chopped onion
3 hard cooked eggs, diced
1/2 cup celery, chopped
4 small sweet pickles, chopped

dressing

1 cup mayonnaise
3/4 teaspoon dill weed
1 teaspoon prepared mustard
dash of wine vinegar

Combine dressing ingredients, add to warm potatoes and mix lightly. Add remaining salad ingredients and mix well. Refrigerate for several hours. Decorate salad with sliced pimento, stuffed green olives, onion, and green bell pepper rings.

....Grandmother says that the secret to an excellent potato salad is to peel the potatoes before you cook them and salt the water generously.

Alzada Black – Ponca City, Oklahoma

sweet potatoes and apricots

1 large can sweet potatoes
1 small can apricot halves
pecans

sauce

1-1/4 cup brown sugar
2 tablespoons cornstarch
1 teaspoon grated orange rind
1/4 teaspoon cinnamon
1 cup apricot juice
2 tablespoons butter

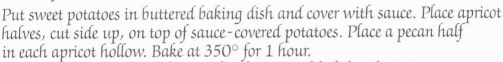

Put sweet potatoes in buttered baking dish and cover with sauce. Place apricot halves, cut side up, on top of sauce-covered potatoes. Place a pecan half in each apricot hollow. Bake at 350° for 1 hour.
....This is excellent with ham or for that special holiday dinner.

For sauce, mix all ingredients and cook until clear and thickened.

Jane Armstrong – Dallas, Texas

sweet potato balls

cornflakes
2 egg whites
3 cups mashed sweet potatoes
1/2 cup butter
1/2 cup pecans, chopped
1 teaspoon salt
2 tablespoons brown sugar
1/2 teaspoon cinnamon
1/2 teaspoon nutmeg
1/2 cup pineapple, crushed
large marshmallows

Crush cornflakes by rolling between folds of wax paper. Set aside. Beat egg whites until stiff. Blend potatoes, butter, pecans, salt, brown sugar, cinnamon, nutmeg, and pineapple until well mixed. Shape mixture around marshmallows; then roll each ball in egg whites and then in cornflakes. Deep fry.

....May be prepared a day in advance and fried at the last minute. Serves 6.

Rainee Barkhorn – Honolulu, Hawaii

minted yams for lamb

3 1-pound cans yams
2 tablespoons butter
1/3 cup mint jelly
1/4 cup water
1/2 teaspoon grated orange peel
2 tablespoons slivered almonds
dash of salt

Melt butter in a large skillet, add jelly, water, grated orange peel, and salt. Boil until jelly melts. Add yams, cook over low heat for 10 minutes, turning occasionally. Sprinkle with nuts. Serve with lamb roast, chops or any roast. Serves 6.

Jessie Paris – Ponca City, Oklahoma

scalloped tomatoes

6 slices stale bread (2 days old,
    left to air overnight, crusts
    removed, crumbled)
6 large tomatoes
1/2 cup onion
1 teaspoon onion salt
1 tablespoon sugar
1 teaspoon poultry seasoning
1/2 teaspoon curry powder
1/2 cup parsley

Peel and slice tomatoes and set aside. Chop parsley fine, chop onions and measure. Place parsley and onions in medium size bowl, mix with onion salt, sugar, poultry seasoning, and curry powder. Blend well then add bread crumbs. Mix well.

Butter casserole well. Layer seasoned crumb mixture with sliced tomatoes in casserole. Continue with several layers until filled. Top with 6 to 8 pieces of butter. Bake at 300° for 1 hour.

....An alternate way of doing this is to scoop out tomatoes, chop pulp, and mix with the crumbs and seasoning and put into the drained tomato shells. Top with butter and bake at 350° for 20 minutes.

Nancy Kennedy – Honolulu, Hawaii

picnic loaf

1 loaf sourdough bread, unsliced
5 medium tomatoes
4 scallions, whites only
1/2 cup ripe olives
1/2 cup green, pimento stuffed olives
4 tablespoons fresh parsley
4 tablespoons Parmesan cheese
1/4 teaspoon dried thyme
1/2 teaspoon dried oregano
3 tablespoons olive oil
3 tablespoons dry white wine
salt and pepper to taste

Cut off ends from the bread. Using a long handled fork, scoop out enough of the bread to make a long, hollow tube with a 1/2 inch crust, reserving the bread crumbs. Peel, seed, and finely chop tomatoes. In a large mixing bowl, combine the bread crumbs with the tomatoes, thinly sliced scallions, chopped olives, chopped parsley, cheese, thyme and oregano. Mix gently but thoroughly. Add the olive oil, white wine, salt and pepper. Mix again. Cover one end of the loaf and fill with the mixture, packing it firmly. Wrap loaf with aluminum foil, and chill for 24 hours. To serve, cut in 1/2 inch slices with a sharp knife. Serves 6.

Virginia Stringer – Honolulu, Hawaii

squash casserole

1/2 stick butter
1 pound yellow squash
1 green pepper
1 can tomatoes
1 cup cheddar cheese
1 can mushroom soup

Slice squash, dice pepper, drain tomatoes and grate cheese. Layer squash and other ingredients in order listed. Cover with cracker crumbs and dot with butter. Bake at 350° for 1 to 1-1/2 hours. Use a 9 x 11 inch pyrex dish and cover with foil for part of the baking time.

Patti Bowker – Ponca City, Oklahoma

spinach artichoke

1 package chopped frozen spinach
3 eggs
2 jars marinated artichoke
1/2 pound mushrooms
2 onions
1-1/2 cups grated cheddar
salt and pepper to taste

Thaw spinach and drain well. Beat eggs lightly. Drain artichokes and save marinade. Set all of these aside.

Slice mushrooms and chop onions and saute in some of the marinade until soft. Add the artichokes, cheddar cheese, eggs, seasoning and then spinach. Blend well. Turn into a well-greased pie plate and bake at 350° for 45 minutes. Serve warm or cold.

Freida Alexander – Beverly Hills, California

oriental spinach

2 tablespoons onion
1/2 pound fresh mushrooms
1 16-ounce can bean sprouts
1 pound fresh spinach
2 tablespoons sesame seeds
1/2 cup sesame or peanut oil
1/4 cup soy sauce
2 tablespoons lemon juice
1/2 teaspoon sugar
1/2 teaspoon pepper
1/2 cup water chestnuts

Slice onions and mushrooms and set aside. Drain liquid from canned bean sprouts, then place the sprouts in cold water and soak for several hours or until crisp and drain. Wash spinach in cold water, cut off tough stems, dry and chill. Toast the sesame seeds lightly in 350° oven, allow to cool.

In a small bowl, combine oil, soy sauce, chopped onion, sesame seeds, lemon juice, sugar and pepper. Let dressing set for at least 1 hour. Put spinach leaves, mushrooms, bean sprouts and water chestnuts in a salad bowl. Pour dressing over salad and toss thoroughly. Serves 8.

Pat Evans – Ponca City, Oklahoma

spinach mold with sauce

mold

2 packages frozen chopped spinach
2 3-ounce packages cream cheese with chives
1 can condensed cream of mushroom soup
2 eggs

sauce

1/4 cup butter
1 pound fresh mushrooms
1/2 cup green onions
2 tablespoons flour
1/2 cup beef stock

1/8 teaspoon salt
1/8 teaspoon pepper
1 teaspoon dill
1 cup sour cream

For the mold, drain spinach well. Blend with cheese, soup and eggs in food processor. Pour into a well-greased 4-1/2 cup ring mold. Place mold in 2 inches of water in a baking dish and bake at 350° for 50 minutes or until inserted knife comes away clean. Let mold stand 5 to 10 minutes, then run knife around edges and turn onto serving platter.

For the sauce, clean the mushrooms and mince with green onions. Melt butter over medium heat and add onions and mushrooms. Stir in flour and beef stock gradually, stirring until thickened. Add salt, dill, and pepper to taste. Let cook 10 minutes, then add sour cream. Reheat just to boiling point and pour into center of spinach mold. Serves 4-6.

Freida Alexander – Beverly Hills, California

spinach souffle

2 packages frozen chopped spinach
1 carton (8 ounces) sour cream
1 envelope dry onion soup mix
1 can water chestnuts
1/4 cup butter

Defrost and drain spinach. Chop water chestnuts and cook in butter over medium heat for 5 minutes. Mix spinach, sour cream, soup mix and chestnuts together. Put in ungreased pyrex or ovenproof bowl and bake at 350° for 30 minutes.

Cynnie Belle Ayau – Honolulu, Hawaii

ratatouille a la nicoise

1 pound eggplant
1 pound zucchini
1 teaspoon salt
6 tablespoons flour
1/2 to 3/4 cup olive oil
1 large onion
2 green peppers
2 garlic cloves
2 pounds tomatoes
salt and freshly ground pepper
6 tablespoons parsley
3 tablespoons fresh snipped dill
3 tablespoons grated Parmesan cheese
1 tablespoon fresh basil or
    1/2 teaspoon dried

Peel eggplant and cut crosswise into slices 1/2 inch thick, then cut each slice into strips about 1 inch wide and 2 to 3 inches long. Quarter zucchini lengthwise, the halve crosswise into 2 to 3-inch lengths. Place eggplant and zucchini into medium bowl, sprinkle with salt and toss lightly. Allow to stand for 30 minutes. Drain off all liquid, rinse vegetables and dry thoroughly with paper towels. Toss gently in flour. Heat 3 tablespoons oil in a 12-inch skillet over medium high heat until very hot. Add half the eggplant and zucchini and saute until golden. Transfer to bowl. Add 3 more tablespoons oil and saute remaining eggplant and zucchini. Add to bowl. Place about 2 more tablespoons oil in same skillet, chop onions and saute with green pepper cut into 1/2-inch strips and minced garlic briefly, about 3 to 4 minutes. Peel and seed tomatoes, drain and cut into 1/2-inch strips and add, along with salt and pepper to taste, and cook about 5 minutes longer.

Place 1/3 of tomato-onion mixture in an 8 to 10-inch skillet or heatproof casserole. Sprinkle with 1/3 each of parsley, dill, cheese, and basil and top with half of the eggplant-zucchini mixture. Continue layering, ending with herbs and cheese. Cover and simmer gently over low heat for 10 minutes, or until most of the liquid has evaporated. (Make sure heat remains low to prevent scorching.) Serve hot, at room temperature or chilled.

Marylou Brogan – Honolulu, Hawaii

sage

sage

Mediterranean origin...still growing wild along the shores from Spain to the Adriatic, this herb can attain the height of 15 inches when grown in a window garden ...sage honey was a luxury in ancient days and today, sage tea is popular in China where it is often preferred to the native brew.

Desserts & Pies

iced zabaglione

8 egg yolks
1/2 lemon with peel sliced
1/2 cup sugar
1 cup dry marsala wine
1 teaspoon unflavored gelatin
2 tablespoons boiling water
3 tablespoons cognac or brandy
2 cups heavy cream
1/2 teaspoon vanilla
1 tablespoon sugar

Whip cream stiff, adding 1/2 teaspoon vanilla and 1 tablespoon sugar, and set aside.

Beat egg yolks, lemon peel and sugar for 3 minutes with an electric beater, or 9 minutes with a hand beater. Remove lemon peel, and fold in the marsala wine. Place egg mixture in the top of a double boiler (the water in the bottom should be boiling slowly). Cook for about 6 minutes, continuing to beat with the beater. Zabaglione is cooked when it stands in soft peaks. Remove from the heat.

Soften gelatin in 1 tablespoon cold water, then dissolve it in boiling water. Add it to the zabaglione stirring slowly. When the mixture is at room temperature, fold in the cognac and whipped cream. Place the zabaglione in individual glasses, or in a crystal or silver bowl, and chill in the refrigerator, 4 or 5 hours. Serve with cookies or French pastry. Serves 8.

Mrs. Luce suggests that you try zabaglione over fresh fruit.

The Hon. Clare Boothe Luce – Honolulu, Hawaii; Washington, D.C.

frozen delight

1 8-ounce package cream cheese
1 12-ounce package frozen, sliced
    strawberries
1 1-pound 4-ounce can pineapple
    chunks, drained
2 tablespoons lemon juice
2 tablespoons honey
1/2 cup mayonnaise
1/2 pint whipping cream
2 bananas
12 large marshmallows
1/2 cup dates
crisp lettuce

Allow cheese to stand at room temperature until softened. Thaw strawberries and save syrup. Drain pineapple. Combine softened cream cheese, syrup, lemon juice and honey. Blend well until smooth. Stir in mayonnaise. Fold in stiffly beaten cream. Fold in bananas cut into small chunks, marshmallows cut into eighths, drained pineapple, sliced dates and sliced strawberries.

Spoon into cans or molds. Cover with foil and freeze until firm. When ready to serve, remove from molds and cut into slices. Arrange on lettuce. Makes 2 quarts. For round slices, save 4 cans of the 20-ounce size and fill 3-1/2 cans with only the top removed. Cover with foil. When ready to use, open other end and push frozen delight out and slice. 3-1/2 cans filled serves 24.

Mitzi Wade – Marietta, Georgia

meringue surprises

2 egg whites
1/8 teaspoon salt
1/2 cup sugar
1 teaspoon vanilla
1 6-ounce package semi-sweet
   chocolate bits

Beat whites and salt until stiff but not dry. Turn to low speed and add sugar gradually, until mixture is stiff and satiny. Fold in vanilla and chocolate bits.

Drop meringue mixture on lightly greased cookie sheet, using small amounts on a spoon. These meringues will not spread so they can be placed close together. They can be made so small that 50 or 60 tiny meringues will fit on one 14 x 17 inch cookie sheet.

Bake at 300° for about 30 minutes. Remove with a spatula and place on a large platter to cool. These are best when baked on the day they are to be served.

Kathryn Murray – Honolulu, Hawaii

marilyn's chocolate dessert

1 12-ounce package chocolate chips
8 eggs
1 pint whipping cream
1-1/2 cups slivered almonds, toasted
1 angel food cake

Melt chocolate chips, cool slightly. Beat eggs well. Pour chocolate over eggs and mix well. Whip cream and add vanilla. Add almonds. Fold cream mixture into chocolate-egg mixture. Pour over angel food cake that has been torn into pieces and chill. Serves 8.

Brenda Lennox – Calgary, Alberta, Canada

tropical flan

1-1/3 cups sugar
4 cups light cream
finely grated rind from 1 large lime
3 tablespoons lime juice
12 egg yolks

Preheat oven to 350° and adjust rack to center of oven. Caramelize 1 cup sugar (reserving remaining 1/3 cup), by placing it in a heavy skillet over moderately high heat. Stir occasionally with a wooden spoon or spatula until sugar starts to melt. Then stir constantly until melted to a smooth caramel. It should be a rich brown but do not let it become too dark or it will have a bitter, burnt taste. If it is not cooked long enough it will be tasteless.

Immediately put the caramelized sugar into a 2-quart souffle dish or other round, ovenproof dish. Using potholders, quickly turn and tilt the dish to coat the bottom and almost all the way up on the sides. Continue to tilt and turn the dish until the caramel stops running. Set aside.

Scald the cream, uncovered in a heavy saucepan or in the top of a double boiler over boiling water. Meanwhile, mix the lime rind and juice together and set aside. In a large mixing bowl, stir the yolks, just to mix. When the cream forms tiny bubbles around the edge and a slightly wrinkled skin on top, remove it from the heat. Add the remaining 1/3 cup sugar and stir to dissolve. Very gradually, just a bit at a time at first, add it to the yolks, stirring constantly. Strain and then gradually stir in the lime rind and juice. Pour into the caramelized dish. Place in a large pan. The pan must not touch the sides of the dish, and must not be deeper than the dish. Pour hot water into the large pan to about 2/3 of the way up the sides of the custard dish. Cover loosely with a cookie sheet or a large piece of aluminum foil.

Bake for 1-1/4 hours, or until small knife inserted into center comes out clean. Do not make any more knife tests than necessary. Do not insert knife all the way to bottom of custard or it will spoil the appearance when inverted. Remove from the hot water and place on rack. Cool, uncovered to room temperature. Refrigerate 10 to 24 hours. Do not skimp on the chilling time. (See note…)

If necessary, cut around the upper edge of the custard to release. Choose a dessert platter with a flat bottom and enough rim to hold the caramel, which will have melted to a sauce. Place the platter upside down over the custard. Carefully invert. Remove the dish. Refrigerate. Serve very cold. Serves 6 to 8.

tropical flan con't

...you may serve a side dish of fruits if you desire.

...if flan is underbaked or if it isn't refrigerated long enough, it will collapse when cut. It is best not to invert it too long before serving. The shiny coating will become dull as it stands. To remove hardened caramel from utensils, place them in the sink and let hot water run over them until caramel disappears.

...this tropical custard, flavored with lime has an exquisite flavor and texture. Best made a day ahead.

Betty and B. Horner – Tulsa, Oklahoma

chocolate surprise dessert

1/2 cup butter or margarine
1 cup all-purpose flour
1 cup peanuts or walnuts
1 8-ounce package cream cheese
1 cup sifted powdered sugar
1 14-ounce carton Cool Whip
2 packages instant chocolate
     pudding mix
3 cups milk
grated chocolate

In a mixing bowl, cut butter into flour until crumbly. Stir in 3/4 cup peanuts or walnuts. Press mixture evenly over bottom of a 13 x 9 x 2 baking dish. Bake at 350° for 20 minutes. Cool.

Meanwhile, in a small mixer bowl, mix softened cream cheese at a low speed until fluffy. Beat in powdered sugar and 1/2 of the Cool Whip. Spread over crust and chill. In a large bowl, combine pudding mix and milk. Beat for 2 minutes. Spoon over cream cheese mixture layer and chill or freeze until firm, several hours or overnight. Top with remaining Cool Whip. Sprinkle with grated chocolate and remaining nuts.

...if frozen, allow to stand 10 to 15 minutes before serving. Serves 16.

Freida Alexander – Beverly Hills, California

cold lemon souffle

mixture #1

16 egg yolks
1 cup sugar
1 cup fresh lemon juice
4 large lemons, rinds only
2 tablespoons plain gelatin
1/2 cup rum
pinch of salt

mixture #2

10 egg whites
1 cup sugar
2 cups heavy whipping cream
1/2 cup pecans

For mixture #1, squeeze lemons to make 1 cup juice. Grate rind from lemons and set aside. Beat yolks until light and fluffy. Add sugar gradually, beating after each addition for approximately 5 minutes. Add lemon juice, rind and salt. Mix well with a wire whisk. Pour mixture into heavy bottomed pan. Place over low heat, stirring with a whisk for about 10 minutes, or until mixture thickens like a custard. Blend gelatin with rum, and add to the hot custard mixture. Whisk until dissolved. Cool.

For mixture #2, chop pecans, but save some halves. Beat egg whites, adding sugar slowly for about 5 minutes. Beat the cream until not too stiff. Fold whites into mixture #1 that has been cooled. Add the whipped cream and fold in gently. Pour into a 1-1/2 quart souffle dish. Put a 3-inch paper collar on souffle dish. Set and decorate with nuts and whipping cream. Freeze. Allow to thaw in refrigerator 1 hour before serving.

Helen Hamilton – Seabury Hall, Maui, Hawaii

hot raspberry souffle

sauce

1 10-ounce package frozen, sweetened raspberries
2 tablespoons almond liqueur

souffle

butter
sugar
3 tablespoons butter
3 tablespoons flour
1/2 cup milk
2 tablespoons sugar
4 large egg yolks
pinch of salt and powdered sugar
1/4 cup almond liqueur
2 10-ounce packages frozen, sweetened raspberries
1/4 cup syrup reserved
3 tablespoons raspberry jam
6 large egg whites (room temp.)
1/4 teaspoon cream of tartar

For sauce: thaw raspberries and place with almond liqueur in blender or food processor, with a steel knife. Whirl a few seconds to partially puree. Remove and set aside.

For souffle: prepare 1-1/2 quart souffle dish. Make collar by cutting piece of wax paper long enough to encircle dish with a few inches of overlap. Fold in half lengthwise and place around dish. Secure with string. Butter dish and wax paper thoroughly and sprinkle with sugar. Set aside.

Melt 3 tablespoons butter in small saucepan over low heat. Stir in flour and blend until smooth. Remove from heat and slowly whisk in milk and sugar. Cook over medium heat stirring constantly until mixture thickens. Remove. Thoroughly beat yolks, almond liqueur, 1/4 cup reserved syrup and jam. Stir in 1/3 hot milk mixture, stirring constantly. Return mixture to pan and cook for 1 minute. Transfer to large bowl and stir in raspberries. Cool. Preheat oven to 375°. Place rack in lower 1/3 of oven. Beat egg whites until foamy. Add cream of tartar and salt and beat until stiff. Fold half of whites gently but thoroughly into raspberry mixture. Carefully fold in remaining whites. Lightly spoon into souffle dish. Bake 35 to 45 minutes, or until deep, golden brown. Sprinkle with powdered sugar and serve immediately with raspberry sauce.

Marylou Brogan – Honolulu, Hawaii

chocolate souffle

1 cup milk
2 ounces unsweetened chocolate
1/2 cup flour
1/2 cup sugar
2/3 cup cold milk
1/4 cup sweet butter
5 eggs, separated

Bring 1 cup of milk to boil with chocolate. Mix remaining milk with sugar and flour. Add this mixture to the hot milk and chocolate. Bring to a boil. Add butter and egg yolks. Whip egg whites until very stiff and fold into the mixture with a wooden spoon. Bake in a buttered pyrex dish at 375° for 15 to 20 minutes.

Maurice Thullier – Aspen, Colorado
Maurice's at the Aspen Alps

mighty mousse

1-1/2 cups semi-sweet chocolate chips
2 eggs
1 tablespoon cognac
pinch of cinnamon
1-1/2 cups half and half, scalding hot

Combine the first 4 ingredients in a blender. Mix briefly. Add half and half and blend thoroughly. Pour into a bowl. Cover and chill until set. Serves 6 to 8.

...it is recommended that this be presented in a large bowl, letting guests serve themselves.

Betty Perry – Honolulu, Hawaii

kahlúa mousse

1/2 cup sugar
1/3 cup water
4 eggs
pinch of salt
2 tablespoons cognac
6 ounces chocolate chips
3 tablespoons Kahlúa
2 cups whipping cream

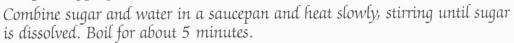

Combine sugar and water in a saucepan and heat slowly, stirring until sugar is dissolved. Boil for about 5 minutes.

Place eggs, salt and chocolate in a blender. Blend until chocolate is smooth. Add sugar syrup in a slow stream as you blend at medium speed. Blend until smooth. Cool for a while, then add Kahlúa and cognac. Pour into a bowl. Place in refrigerator for about 2 hours, until it is chilled and almost stiff. Beat whipping cream until it forms peaks. Use about 2/3 of it and fold it into the chilled mixture. Decorate with remaining whipped cream and chill until ready to serve. Serves 4 to 6.

Pat Evans – Ponca City, Oklahoma

chocolate mousse galliano

4 eggs, separated
1/2 cup sugar
1/2 cup liqueur Galliano
6 squares semi-sweet chocolate
1/4 pound softened sweet butter
1 tablespoon sugar

Beat together egg yolks and 1/2 cup sugar until light and fluffy. Beat in 1/4 cup Galliano for a full 5 minutes. Melt chocolate over hot water. Blend in butter and remaining liqueur. Add this to egg yolk mixture, stirring constantly. Whip egg whites to form soft peaks and beat in 1 tablespoon sugar, until stiff. Fold into chocolate mixture. Chill in serving dish or crème pots.

Filomena Buck – Honolulu, Hawaii

grand marnier-chocolate mousse cups

chocolate cups

10 ounces milk chocolate
3 tablespoons butter

mousse

1-1/2 cups whipping cream
1 tablespoon Grand Marnier
2 tablespoons sugar
2 ounces semi-sweet chocolate
1 ounce unsweetened chocolate
1 tablespoon Grand Marnier
2 eggs
1/4 cup sugar
dash of salt
1 tablespoon grated chocolate

To prepare the chocolate cups, melt the chocolate with the butter in the top of a double boiler, stirring just until combined. Place 8 paper or foil muffin cups in a muffin tin and fill each with approximately 2 tablespoons of the chocolate. Spread evenly around the bottoms and sides. Refrigerate until the form sets, then gently peel off the muffin cups. Place back in the refrigerator.

For the mousse, in a large bowl, beat the whipping cream with the Grand Marnier and sugar until stiff. Remove 1/3 and save for garnish. Melt the semi-sweet and unsweetened chocolate with Grand Marnier. Stir until smooth and set aside. In a small bowl, beat eggs, sugar and salt until fluffy. Whisk both egg and chocolate mixture into whipped cream. Divide into 8 cups and garnish with the extra whipped cream and grated chocolate.

Shannon Lowrey – Honolulu, Hawaii

frozen mousse grand marnier

mousse

2 egg whites
pinch of salt
6 tablespoons sugar
1 cup heavy cream
1/4 cup Grand Marnier
    (more or less to taste)

berry sauce

1 10-ounce package frozen raspberries
      or
1 pint fresh strawberries or raspberries
2 tablespoons sugar
Grand Marnier

To make the mousse, beat egg whites with salt until softly peaked. Gradually add 4 tablespoons of sugar. Beat until meringue is stiff and shiny. Whip cream until stiff and add 2 tablespoons sugar. Gently blend Grand Marnier into cream and fold in egg whites. Turn into a 1-quart mold, or individual molds. Freeze. Serve with berry sauce. Serves 4. Recipe easily doubles or triples.

For the sauce, if using frozen berries, defrost just enough to drain excess juice. Add Grand Marnier to taste and stir. If using fresh berries, clean berries, sweeten with sugar and chill. Add Grand Marnier, stir and serve over mousse.

Claire Smith – Dallas, Texas

strawberries amaretto

4 cups large strawberries
1-1/2 cups sour cream
1 cup brown sugar
1/2 cup amaretto

Wash and halve all but 8 berries. Mix remaining ingredients and fold in berries. Garnish each serving with a whole berry and a sprig of mint. Serves 8.

Carol Collins – San Francisco, California

elegant strawberry dessert

1/2 pound graham crackers
3/4 cup soft butter
2-1/2 cups powdered sugar
2 eggs
1 quart frozen strawberries
3 tablespoons cornstarch
1/2 cup water
1/2 pint whipping cream
1 tablespoon powdered sugar
1/2 teaspoon vanilla

first layer

Crush graham crackers. Place 2/3 of the crumbs on the bottom of a greased
9 x 13-inch cake pan. Reserve remaining crumbs.

second layer

Beat butter and 2-1/2 cups sugar until creamy. Add eggs, one at a time, beating
well after each. Spoon gently over crust layer.

third layer

Drain juice from strawberries and add cornstarch and water. Boil until thick.
Cool. Add strawberries and pour over second layer.

fourth layer

Whip cream and add 1 tablespoon sugar and vanilla. Spread over third layer.

fifth layer

Sprinkle remaining crumbs on top. Refrigerate for 24 hours. Cut into squares.
Serves 14-16.

Connie Baldwin – Honolulu, Hawaii

coconut mousse

1 cup coconut milk
1 cup half and half
3 tablespoons gelatin
1/3 cup water
1 cup sugar
2 cups coconut
1 teaspoon almond extract
1-1/2 pints heavy cream

Dissolve gelatin in water. In a saucepan, heat half and half and coconut milk to the boiling point. Then add gelatin mixture, sugar and dissolve. Cool and add freshly grated coconut. In a bowl, beat heavy cream and almond extract until stiff. Fold into coconut mixture and pour mousse into an 8-cup mold. Chill the mousse until it is firm. Serves 10.

…you may sprinkle with grated coconut to serve.

Patricia Lang – Honolulu, Hawaii

peaches flambé

6 tablespoons sugar
6 tablespoons butter
juice of 1 orange
peel of half a lemon
peel of half an orange
6 tablespoons Cointreau or
    other orange liqueur
10 peaches
brandy

Caramelize sugar until medium gold in color. Add the butter, orange and lemon peels, orange juice and orange liqueur. Simmer a few minutes. Peel the peaches and cut in eighths. Add peaches to sugar mixture and simmer again for a few minutes. Add brandy and ignite.

…may be served over vanilla ice cream.

Cleo Evans – Honolulu, Hawaii

les crepes aux pommes flambés au calvados

crepe batter

5 ounces flour
2 eggs
2 tablespoons sugar
2 cups hot milk
2 ounces clarified butter
pinch of salt

filling

6 apples, sliced
12 tablespoons butter
12 tablespoons sugar
1/2 cup calvados

Pour the flour into a large bowl with eggs, sugar and salt. Mix well with a whip or mixer while adding the hot milk and clarified butter. Set batter aside.

Grease the pan with 1 teaspoon butter and saute sliced apples. Sprinkle with 1 teaspoon of sugar and cook until golden. Set apples aside until ready to roll crepes.

To make crepes, pour enough batter into the crepe pan to cover the bottom, (about 2 tablespoons). Cook for about 1 minute. Turn it over with a spatula and fry the other side. Place crepes one by one on a buttered baking dish and keep warm. When ready to serve crepes, roll each crepe after filling with apple mixture, only using half of the mixture for the filling. The other half will be re-cooked with 1 teaspoon sugar added. Cook until sugar caramelizes.

Put crepes in a flambé pan, pour apple mixture over crepes. Sprinkle entire pan with sugar and hot calvados and flame.

....calvados is an apple liqueur.

Ed Sullivan – Honolulu, Hawaii
Hyatt Regency, Waikiki

hattie's peach pie

8 peaches
1 cup sugar
1/2 teaspoon cinnamon
1 tablespoon flour
1 egg

Mix dry ingredients. Slightly beat egg, mix in dry ingredients. Add sliced peaches, stir together. Put into pie shell. Bake 35 to 40 minutes at 400°.

Sue Mertz, Ponca City, Oklahoma

bananas foster

2 tablespoons butter
4 tablespoons brown sugar
1 tablespoon water
2 bananas, quartered
1 ounce or more light rum
ice cream

Melt butter, add water and brown sugar and cook until caramelized. Stir in bananas, quartered (cut in half, if desired). Cook until tender. Add rum and pour over ice cream.

…some cooks add a pinch of cinnamon, or use brandy.

…raisins and toasted slivered almonds can be added to this too…yummy!

Sugar and Spice

223

apple kuchen

1 package yellow cake mix
1/2 cup margarine
1/2 cup coconut
1/2 cup pecans, chopped
1 can apple pie filling
1/2 cup sugar and 1 teaspoon
    cinnamon, mixed
1 egg or 2 egg yolks
1 cup sour cream

Combine first 4 ingredients in a bowl, cutting in the margarine. Press into a 9-1/2 x 13-inch pan between 1/2 to 1 inch up the sides. Bake 10 minutes at 400°. Pour apple filling over warm crust. Sprinkle with sugar and cinnamon mixture. Beat egg and sour cream together. Pour over apple mixture. Bake at 350° for about 25 minutes until crust browns. Very tasty!

Elsie Mornhinweg – Perry, Oklahoma

blueberry sour cream pie

crust

1-3/4 cups graham cracker crumbs
1/2 cup walnuts
1/2 teaspoon cinnamon
1/2 cup butter

filling

1 quart blueberries, raspberries or sliced
    peaches or any fresh fruit
1 pint sour cream
1/2 cup sugar

For the crust, roll crackers between wax paper until crumbled, then measure. Chop walnuts and measure. Combine crumbs, nuts and spices and mix well with softened butter. Press into bottom and up along sides of a 9-inch pie plate.

For the filling, blend fresh fruit with sour cream and sugar. Pour into crust. Bake at 350° for 20 to 25 minutes…the pie might not look done when removed from the oven, but it thickens while cooling. Cool in refrigerator.

Linda Janovic – New York, New York

pear pie in cheddar crust

crust

1 cup all-purpose flour
1/4 teaspoon salt
1/3 cup shortening
1/2 cup (2 ounces) shredded cheddar
    cheese
3 to 4 tablespoons ice water

filling

6 medium pears, peeled and sliced
1/2 cup sugar
1 teaspoon lemon peel
3 tablespoons cornstarch
3 tablespoons lemon juice

topping

1/2 cup each, flour and sugar
1/2 teaspoon each, ginger and cinnamon
1/4 teaspoon mace
1/3 cup butter

For the crust, in a medium bowl, combine flour and salt. With a pastry blender or 2 knives used scissor-fashion, cut in shortening until mixture resembles coarse crumbs. Mix in cheese. Sprinkle in ice water a spoonful at a time, tossing with a fork after each addition until pastry is just moist enough to hold together. Form dough into a ball. Flatten slightly on a lightly floured surface. Prepare pie shell as for a single crust pie.

Prepare the filling by combining all ingredients and pouring into unbaked pie shell.

For the topping, cut butter into ingredients and cover filling. Bake at 400° for 45 minutes. Serve warm with whipped cream.

Marjorie Wilson – Honolulu, Hawaii

upside-down cherry pie

1 cup sugar
1 cup flour
1 heaping teaspoon baking powder
pinch of salt
3/4 cup milk
1 16 ounce can of cherry pie filling

In a 9 x 11-inch pyrex baking dish, melt 1/2 cup butter. Combine remaining ingredients (except cherries). Then pour the batter over the melted butter. Add the cherries. Bake at 350° till browned on top.

…an easy and tasty dessert. Good for children to make.

Patti Bowker – Ponca City, Oklahoma

cream cheese dessert

1 8-ounce package cream cheese
1 large egg
1 cup powdered sugar
1/4 cup brandy
frozen or fresh fruits in season

Mix all ingredients in a blender except fruit. Pour into parfait glasses and chill well. Top with fruits and fruits' syrup of your choice. Serves 4.

Devon Guard – Honolulu, Hawaii

ritz cracker dessert

3 egg whites
1 cup sugar
1/2 teaspoon baking powder
1 teaspoon vanilla
2/3 cup broken pecans
14 Ritz crackers, broken
1/2 pint whipping cream
powdered sugar, vanilla

Beat egg whites until stiff. Gradually add sugar, baking powder and vanilla. Fold in broken nuts and crackers. Bake in a greased pan, 9 x (10 or 12) x 2 inches, at 325° for 35 minutes.

When cool, cover with whipping cream to which powdered sugar and vanilla have been added. Freeze. Remove 1 hour before serving. Serves 8 to 9.

Betty H. Horner – Tulsa, Oklahoma

impossible pie

4 eggs
1/2 cup margarine
1/2 cup flour
2 cups milk
1 cup sugar
1 cup coconut, shredded
2 teaspoons vanilla
1/4 pint whipping cream

Pour all ingredients except cream into a blender for a few seconds to mix. Pour the mixture into a greased 10-inch pie plate. Bake at 350° for 1 hour. The flour forms the crust, coconut the topping and eggs are the center custard. Decorate with whipped cream.

Barbara Bell – Aspen, Colorado

louisville pie

1 stick melted butter
4 eggs
1 cup granulated sugar
1 cup chopped pecans
1 teaspoon vanilla or
    2 tablespoons bourbon
1 cup white corn syrup
1 cup chocolate chips
1 tablespoon vanilla
1 tablespoon flour

Melt butter. Beat eggs and add all other ingredients. Bake in an uncooked pie crust. Preheat oven to 350° Bake for 35-40 minutes. Top with ice cream or whipped cream. Makes 2 small or 1 extra large pie. This can be frozen.

Claire Johnson – Honolulu, Hawaii

pumpkin pie delight

1 8-ounce package cream cheese
1 egg
1/2 cup sugar
1 teaspoon vanilla
1 teaspoon cinnamon
1 teaspoon mace
1/2 teaspoon ginger
1 cup half and half
2 eggs, beaten
3/4 cup sugar
1 16-ounce can pumpkin
1 9-inch pie dish lined with unbaked pastry.

Garnish: whipped cream, peanut brittle

Cream cheese with electric beater until light and fluffy. Blend in the egg, 1/2 cup sugar and the vanilla. Spread cheese mixture on the bottom of the unbaked pie shell. Blend together remaining ingredients. Pour carefully over cream cheese to form a second layer.

Bake at 425° for 10 minutes. Reduce temperature to 350° and bake 30-35 minutes longer, or until set.

…garnish cooled pie with whipped cream and crushed peanut brittle.

Muffy Ohlmeyer – Beverly Hills, California

lemon pie

1/4 cup lemon juice
4 egg yolks
4 tablespoons water
2 egg whites
1/2 cup sugar

1 cooked, 9-inch pie crust

Put lemon juice, yolks and water in a double boiler and cook until thick. Beat egg whites until stiff. Slowly add the sugar. Add egg white mixture to lemon mixture stirring continuously. Cool 3 to 5 minutes. Pour into cooled pie crust. Top with meringue and brown in oven.

Dorothy Souligny – Ponca City, Oklahoma

frozen lemon pie

1-3/4 cups vanilla wafer crumbs
1 envelope Knox gelatin
2 tablespoons water
1/2 cup honey
1/2 cup sugar
3 eggs, separated
1/3 cup lemon juice
1-1/2 teaspoons grated lemon rind
1/8 teaspoon salt
1/2 teaspoon lemon flavoring
1-1/2 cups canned milk

2 10-inch glass pie dishes

Have the vanilla wafer crumbs crushed and line the bottom and sides of the pie dishes. Set aside. Dissolve gelatin in water and set aside. Cook in a double boiler, the honey, sugar, egg yolks, lemon juice, grated lemon rind and salt until the mixture coats a spoon. Mixture will be runny, but do not boil. When done, remove from heat. Add softened gelatin to the cooked mixture and stir until dissolved. Cool and add lemon flavoring. Beat in a separate bowl the egg whites until stiff. Whip in a separate large bowl very, very cold canned milk until it is fluffy. Fold into the lemon custard mixture, the egg whites and the whipped milk. Pile into the pie plates. Freeze. When served, garnish with a few cherries, or grated nuts or whatever your creativity inspires you to do!

You may also use a 10 x 13-inch loaf pan.

Roberta Lear-Kauffman – Honolulu, Hawaii

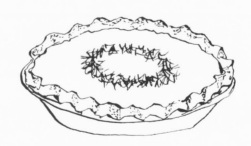

velvet hammer

4 pints vanilla ice cream
1/2 cup orange flavored liqueur
1/2 cup brandy
nutmeg

Place in a blender, 2 pints ice cream, 1/4 cup liqueur and 1/4 cup brandy. Blend until smooth. Do not over-blend. Pour into stemmed glasses and sprinkle nutmeg on top. Repeat procedure with remaining ingredients.

Sugar and Spice

pat crowley's lemon pie

meringue crust

4 egg whites at room temperature
1 cup sugar
1/4 teaspoon cream of tartar

lemon cream filling

8 egg yolks
2 tablespoons lemon rind
6 tablespoons lemon juice
1 cup sugar
1/2 teaspoon salt
2 cups heavy cream

To make one 9-inch crust, beat egg whites and cream of tartar until light and fluffy. Gradually add sugar until peaks form. Generously grease a 9-inch pie pan and gently spread meringue into pan. Build up the sides like a crust. Bake at 275° for 1 hour. Turn off oven and let the crust sit for 2 hours.

For the filling, mix the yolks, rind, juice, sugar and salt in a double boiler. Stir over medium heat for 8 to 10 minutes, until very thick. Let mix cool. Beat the heavy cream and fold in the lemon mix with the cream. Pour into cooled shell. Sprinkle some extra lemon "zest" on top of pie. Refrigerate overnight.

Pat Crowley – Beverly Hills, California

pumpkin pie

mixture #1

4 eggs, beaten
1 29-ounce can pumpkin
1-1/2 cups sugar
3-1/2 teaspoons pumpkin pie spice
1 teaspoon salt
2 13-ounce cans evaporated milk

Combine all ingredients and mix together until well blended. Pour into a lightly greased 9 x 13-inch baking dish.

mixture #2

1 stick butter
1 package spice cake mix
1/2 cup chopped nuts

Mix butter into cake mix until crumbly (like pie dough). Sprinkle on top of pie filling mixture. Sprinkle nuts over top. Bake at 350° for 1 hour or until done. Serve with whipped cream. Serves 15.

Marilyn Goss – Honolulu, Hawaii

orange-yogurt popsicles

1/2 large can frozen orange juice, thawed
1 pint thick, plain yogurt
1 teaspoon vanilla
drinking straws

Freeze (after combining all ingredients) in small dixie cups (3-ounce) with 1/2 straw stuck in each. Healthy alternative to popsicles, ice cream, etc.

Barbara Bell – Aspen, Colorado

chocolate coated banana pops

6 bananas
1 12-ounce package chocolate chips
6 tablespoons peanut oil

Peel and cut bananas in half lengthwise. Stick a wooden stick into each banana half and freeze on a cookie sheet for 1 hour. This is important so that chocolate coating will cover better.

Melt chocolate chips in the top of a double boiler over hot (not boiling) water. Add oil and stir until smooth. Keep warm over water while dipping. Take bananas from freezer a few at a time. Dip and roll them into chocolate coating, covering all surfaces. If desired, roll in chopped nuts and freeze.

Barbara Bell – Aspen, Colorado

wonderful walnut pie

pastry for a 9-inch pie crust
filling
1 8-ounce package cream cheese
1/2 cup sugar
1 teaspoon vanilla
1 egg
1 cup chopped walnuts

topping
2 eggs
1/4 cup sugar
1 cup light corn syrup
1 teaspoon vanilla

For the filling, combine softened cream cheese with sugar, vanilla and egg. Place in the pie crust and add walnuts on top of cream cheese mixture.

For the topping, beat all ingredients together and pour on top of nuts. Bake at 375° for 35-40 minutes.

Patricia Kelley Hemmeter – Honolulu, Hawaii

apricot icebox pudding

1 can halved apricots
1/2 cup butter
2 eggs
1 cup powdered sugar
1-1/2 pounds vanilla wafers
1/2 cup pecans, chopped
1/2 pint whipping cream

Drain apricots well. Melt butter in a double boiler. Beat eggs and powdered sugar together and add to melted butter. Cook over boiling water, stirring constantly until thickened.

Roll or grind vanilla wafers and press into a 10 x 15 x 1-inch pan (reserve some for topping). Pour the custard mixture evenly over crumb crust. Sprinkle with chopped pecans. Layer halved apricots evenly over pecans. Then, cover all with whipped cream. Sprinkle remaining crumbs over cream. Chill overnight and cut into squares.

Maxine Van Winkle Treat – Santa Cruz, California

sally's grandmother's ice cream

1-1/2 quarts cream or whole milk
6 eggs
3-1/2 cups sugar
4 tablespoons vanilla extract
2/3 tablespoon lemon extract
2/3 tablespoon almond extract

Place 1 pint milk or cream in a large pan. Place pan in a larger pan of boiling water, or use a very large double boiler, and heat.

Beat eggs while adding sugar. Continue beating for 5 minutes. Add egg and sugar mixture into hot milk, stirring constantly until eggs are cooked (mixture will coat a silver spoon). Pour mixture through a sieve into ice cream freezer. Add extracts. Stir in enough milk or cream to fill freezer to within 1-1/2 inches of top. Freeze. Makes 1-1/2 gallons.

…always use 4 eggs for every gallon your freezer makes.

Beulah Vanselous Edwards

rum chocolate pecan pie

crust #1

1-1/4 cups pecans
3 tablespoons sugar
2 tablespoons butter
1/4 cup unsifted flour

Chop pecans until very fine. Combine all ingredients and blend well. Then press into a greased, 9-inch pie pan. Bake at 400° for 8 to 10 minutes.

or

crust #2

3 squares semi-sweet chocolate
2 tablespoons butter
1-1/4 cup whole blanched almonds

Toast almonds lightly in hot oven. Chop until fine. Melt butter and chocolate and blend in almonds. Refrigerate mixture for 30 to 45 minutes. Press into a greased 9-inch pie pan. Refrigerate for 2 hours before filling.

filling

2 squares unsweetened chocolate
2 cups pecans
1 cup heavy cream
1/2 cup butter
2 egg yolks
2 cups powdered sugar
1/4 teaspoon salt
1/4 cup dark rum
1 teaspoon lemon juice

Melt chocolate in a double boiler and cool. Chop pecans coarsely and set aside. Whip cream and set aside. In a large bowl blend together the butter, egg yolks, sugar, salt, dark rum and lemon juice. Beat at a high speed until smooth and fluffy. Stir in cooled chocolate. Blend until smooth. Fold in pecans. Then fold in cream. Pour mixture into one of the pie crusts given above and chill overnight. Remove from refrigerator 1 hour before serving.

topping

1 cup heavy cream
2 tablespoons sugar
2 teaspoons dark rum

Whip ingredients together. Pour into a pastry tube and decorate top of pie mixture before serving.

Helen Hamilton – Seabury Hall – Maui, Hawaii

ginger

ginger

Chinese origin...it was the "status spice" when Elizabeth I employed a chef-artist to fashion portraits of honored guests in gingerbread...today's gingerbread characters and houses may owe their fame to birthday cakes given to Peter the Great at his birth...one, a one hundred and fifty pound gingerbread modeled after the Kremlin.

Cakes & Pastries

"dadows" gingerbread

butter the size of a walnut
1/2 cup sugar
1/2 cup sorghum or molasses
1 egg
1 large cup flour with 1 teaspoon soda
1 teaspoon ginger
1 teaspoon cinnamon
salt

Combine all ingredients and mix thoroughly. Add 3/4 cup boiling water. Pour into greased 8 x 8-inch pan. Bake at 350° for 30 minutes.

This recipe is over 100 years old. Nancy was Sally's great-grandmother, an Oklahoma Pioneer Woman.

Nancy Hall Edwards – Ponca City, Oklahoma

zucotto

1 12 to 16-ounce pound cake
4 tablespoons cognac
3 tablespoons Galliano, Amaretto,
     or Cointreau
3 cups heavy cream
1 cup or less powdered sugar
2 ounces almonds
4 ounces filberts, pecans, or
     macadamia nuts
7 ounces bittersweet or semi-sweet
     chocolate pieces

Line a half-sphere mold, (8 inch diameter) 2 quart capacity, with cheese cloth. Cut thin pound cake slices diagonally, moisten with cognac and liqueur, and line the mold with points of cake on bottom, at the center. Whip cream into soft peaks. Add sugar, mix in nuts (which have all been toasted and chopped), and 1/2 of the chocolate bits. Spoon 1/2 of the cream mixture into the mold, lining evenly. Melt remaining chocolate over warm water, and combine with remaining cream mixture. Spoon into mold and fill to top. Arrange more cake slices over top, cover with aluminum foil, refrigerate overnight or freeze.

If frozen, take out of freezer and put in refrigerator for at least 2 hours before serving. Unmold onto plate and serve.

….This is excellent when frozen.

Susan Shultz – Paradise Valley, Arizona
….writer, <u>Beverly Hills Diet</u> and sequel

coconut cream cake

1 18-1/2-ounce package regular white
   cake mix (not pudding type)
1 3-1/2-ounce can flaked coconut
1-1/2 cups water
2 egg whites
1 8-1/2-ounce can cream of coconut
1 12-ounce carton frozen whipped
   topping, thawed

Combine cake mix, 1 cup coconut, water and egg whites. Beat for 2 minutes at highest speed of electric mixer. Reduce speed to low, beat for 1 minute. Pour batter into a greased 12 x 9 x 2-inch baking pan. Bake at 350° for 25-30 minutes or until pick comes from center clean. Cool cake for 10 minutes.

Punch holes in the top of cake with toothpick. Pour cream of coconut over cake while still warm. Spread whipped topping over cake. Sprinkle with remaining coconut. Cover and chill at least 4 hours. Cut into squares to serve. Serves 15-16.

Kay Yeary – Ponca City, Oklahoma

mele's hawaiian wedding cakes

1/2 cup butter
2 tablespoons sugar
1 tablespoon vanilla
1 cup cake flour
1 cup pecans, chopped
powdered sugar

Cream together butter and sugar. Add vanilla, flour and nuts. Mix well. Roll dough into small balls, and place on a greased baking sheet. Bake at 300° for 45 minutes. Roll in additional powdered sugar while still warm.

Mele Majors – Dallas, Texas

pasticcini di napoli

pastry
2 cups sifted flour
pinch of salt
1/2 cup sugar
1/2 cup butter
2 egg yolks
grated rind of 1 lemon

filling
3 cups ricotta cheese
6 tablespoons powdered sugar
2 egg yolks
pinch of cinnamon
1 teaspoon grated lemon rind
4 tablespoons raisins (optional)

For pastry, sift flour, salt, and sugar into a bowl. Cut in butter with pastry blender to distribute butter evenly through flour mixture. Add egg yolks, one at a time, mixing with a wooden spoon after each addition. Blend in lemon rind. Work dough with hands until it is manageable and clears sides of bowl. If necessary, add a little water to hold the dough together. Turn out onto a lightly floured board, and knead quickly until smooth. Wrap in wax paper and refrigerate 1 or 2 hours. Roll out to 1/4 inch thickness. Cut pastry into rounds to fill muffin cups. Grease muffin cups lightly and line with pastry. Preheat oven to 350°

Combine ricotta with remaining ingredients and blend well with a wooden spoon. Fill prepared pastry sections. Cut leftover pastry into small strips and criss-cross strips over filling. Trim edges. Bake 40-45 minutes. Cool in oven. Serves 8 to 10.

Angela G. Mancinelli – Honolulu, Hawaii

butter pecan elegance cake

1/2 cup mashed bananas
1 package yellow cake mix (2 layer size)
1 package butter pecan instant
    pudding (4 serving size)
4 eggs
1 cup water
1/4 cup oil
1/2 cup finely chopped pecans (optional)

Combine all ingredients in a large bowl. Blend well, then beat at medium
speed of electric mixer for 4 minutes. Pour into a greased and floured 10-inch tube
pan. Bake at 350° for 50 minutes, or until cake tester inserted in center comes
out clean and cake begins to pull away from sides of pan. Do not underbake!
Cool in pan for 15 minutes, remove from pan and finish cooling on rack. Top with
powdered sugar glaze and with banana slices and pecan halves if desired.

Beth Bowlen – Honolulu, Hawaii
Sally's daughter

zwiebach cake

3 eggs well beaten
1 cup sugar (scant)
1 cup zwiebach crumbs
1 cup chopped nuts
dash of salt and flavoring

Beat eggs until thick. Add sugar, crumbs, nuts and flavoring. Bake in a well-
greased square pan in a moderate oven 350° for 40 minutes. Remove from
pan while hot. Spread with jam. Leave for 24 hours before serving. Serve with
whipped cream or Cool Whip.

....the recipe dates back to 1927.

Jessie Brown – Honolulu, Hawaii

linzertorte

1-1/2 cups all purpose flour
1/8 teaspoon ground cloves
1/4 teaspoon cinnamon
1 cup finely ground almonds
1/2 cup sugar
1 teaspoon grated lemon peel
2 hard boiled egg yolks, mashed
1 cup unsalted butter
2 raw egg yolks, lightly beaten
1 teaspoon vanilla extract
1-1/2 cups raspberry jam
1 egg, lightly beaten
2 teaspoons light cream
powdered sugar

Sift the flour, cloves, and cinnamon together in a deep mixing bowl. Add the almonds, sugar, lemon peel, and mashed egg yolks. Beat in the butter, raw egg yolks and vanilla extract. Continue to beat until mixture is smooth and doughy.

Form dough into a ball, wrap it in wax paper, and refrigerate it for at least 1 hour or until firm. Remove about 3/4 of the dough. Return the rest to the refrigerator.

With a pastry brush, lightly butter a 9-inch round false-bottom cake pan (with 1 to 1-1/2-inch sides). Add the dough and with your fingers, press and push it out so that it covers the bottom and sides of pan. Make the shell about 1/4 inch thick. Spoon in the raspberry jam and spread it over the bottom of the shell. On a floured surface, with a rolling pin, roll out the rest of the dough into a 9 x 6-inch rectangle, about 1/4 inch thick. With a sharp knife, cut dough into strips. Lay one strip across the center of the jam and flank that strip on each side with one placed half way between center and sides of pan. Rotate the pan slightly to your left and repeat the pattern with 3 strips so that they create "X's" in a lattice-like effect. Run a knife around the pan to loosen the part of bottom dough that extends above the strips. Press down lightly along border.

With a pastry brush, coat all exposed pastry with lightly beaten whole egg combined with cream. Refrigerate for 30 minutes. Preheat oven to 350.° Bake the torte in the center of the oven for 45-50 minutes or until lightly browned. Allow to cool, then slip down the outside rim. Sprinkle with powdered sugar.
Serve at room temperature.

Hans Strasser – Honolulu, Hawaii
Prince Kuhio Hotel, Waikiki

jewish coffee cake

1 cup sugar
1 cup butter
3 unbeaten eggs
2 cups flour
1 teaspoon soda
1 teaspoon baking powder
1/8 teaspoon salt
1 cup sour cream
1 teaspoon vanilla

filling:

1/2 cup chopped nuts
2 tablespoons melted butter
1 teaspoon cinnamon
2 tablespoons flour
3/4 cup sugar

Cream together sugar and butter. Add eggs one at a time. Sift flour, soda, baking powder and salt, add alternately to sugar and butter mixture with sour cream and vanilla. Combine all ingredients for filling. Grease and flour bundt pan or tube pan. Pour 1/2 batter, 1/2 filling, then repeat. Bake 350° for 45 minutes.

Sugar and Spice

carrot cake and frosting

2 cups sugar
1 cup Mazola oil
4 eggs
3 cups grated carrots
1/2 cup walnuts, chopped
1/2 cup chopped pineapple,
　　well drained
1/2 cup shredded coconut
1/4 cup pineapple juice
2 cups flour
2 teaspoons soda
2 teaspoons cinnamon
2 teaspoons baking powder
1+ teaspoon salt

Cream sugar and oil. Add unbeaten eggs one at a time, beating well after each addition. Sift together dry ingredients, add along with remaining ingredients. Bake in an ungreased 9 x 13-inch pan, or in layer pans at 350° for 40 minutes, or until done. It will be like custard until it tests done. When cool, frost with my cream cheese frosting.

cream cheese frosting

4 cups or 1 pound package
　　powdered sugar
4 ounces cream cheese
　　(room temperature)
1/4 cup soft butter
1 teaspoon vanilla
3 tablespoons buttermilk

Combine all ingredients and beat with an electric mixer until creamy. Enjoy!

Patricia Kelley Hemmeter – Honolulu, Hawaii

rum cake

1 package Pillsbury Plus cake mix
4 eggs
1-3/4 ounce package instant vanilla pudding
1/2 cup oil
1/2 cup rum
1/2 cup chopped pecans or black walnuts

topping

1/4 cup water
1 cup sugar
1/4 pound margarine

Mix all ingredients for cake except nuts for 2 minutes in a mixer. Grease and flour a bundt pan and pour in batter. Bake in a preheated oven at 350° for 1 hour. Pierce top with an ice pick and drizzle topping over cake completely. Remove from pan.

For the topping, combine ingredients and bring to a boil until margarine is melted and sugar dissolved. Drizzle over cake.

....Great with Mexican food.

Sugar and Spice

devil's food cake

1 cup sugar
1 cup butter
2 eggs separated
1/3 cup cocoa
1/2 cup buttermilk
1 teaspoon soda
1-1/2 cups flour
1 teaspoon baking powder

Cream sugar, butter and egg yolks together and add cocoa which has been moistened to a thin paste with hot water. Mix soda and buttermilk together. Sift flour and baking powder together and add alternately with buttermilk mixture to sugar mixture and beat thoroughly. Add beaten egg whites carefully. Blend well. Bake at 350° for 30-35 minutes. Use any icing.

Florence Wallace – Ponca City, Oklahoma

the best chocolate cake in the world

1 package chocolate fudge cake mix
1 small package chocolate pudding mix
1 cup sour cream
4 eggs
1/2 cup warm water
1/2 cup oil
3 tablespoons melted butter
1 12-ounce package chocolate chips

In a large bowl, add ingredients in order listed and mix together very well. Turn into a well-greased bundt pan and bake at 350° for 50-60 minutes. Leave in pan for 10 minutes before turning on to cake plate. Drizzle your favorite chocolate icing on top or sprinkle with sifted powdered sugar.

....This is a delicious cake, good for school affairs. Frost with strawberry icing below.

Erin Pell – Honolulu, Hawaii

strawberry icing

2 cups powdered sugar
1 stick sweet butter (barely softened)
3 medium strawberries (more if you
      like it pinker)

Hand beat the butter, then gradually add the sugar, using a hand-held electric mixer, and add the strawberries. When it is blended, (do not overbeat) frost the cake.

....Make 2 separate batches if you need to double it.

Linda Janovic – New York, New York

chocolate cake with orange liqueur

6 ounces sugar
8 eggs
1/2 cup flour
1 ounce cornstarch
1-1/2 ounces cocoa
1 pint whipping cream
1 pound chocolate
4 ounces butter
4 ounces water
3-1/2 ounces sugar
1 ounce orange liqueur
chocolate shavings
powdered sugar

Mix sugar and 5 of the eggs, and beat in a stainless steel bowl over medium heated steam table or double boiler until you have doubled the original volume. Remove from heat and continue beating until cooled off. With your hand, slowly blend in flour, cornstarch and cocoa. Very carefully pour into a buttered, 8-inch round cake mold and bake immediately at 350° for 30 minutes. While still hot, remove cake from pan and let cool.

During the baking, prepare the chocolate mousse. Beat the cream until whipped solidly. Melt the chocolate with 1-1/2 spoons of water, then add the butter and 3 remaining eggs. While the mixture is still warm, fold in the whipped cream and refrigerate.

Bring 4 ounces of water together with 3-1/2 ounces sugar, to a boil; cool, then add 1 ounce orange liqueur. Soak the sponge cake with this mixture. When the chocolate mousse has cooled, take out and spread evenly over the cake. Put back in the refrigerator for 3 hours and chill completely. Decorate with chocolate shavings and powdered sugar.

Fred Hellekes – Liberty House
Honolulu, Hawaii

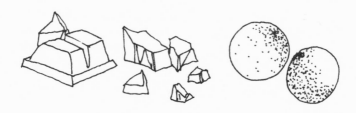

macadamia mocha cheesecake

1-1/2 cups chocolate cookie crumbs
1 cup Hawaiian Holiday finely ground
    macadamia nuts
1/2 teaspoon cinnamon
1 stick melted butter
1 cup sugar
3 eggs
1-1/2 pounds cream cheese, softened
8 ounces semi-sweet chocolate,
    melted
2 tablespoons cocoa
1 teaspoon instant Kona coffee
1 teaspoon vanilla
3 cups sour cream
3/4 cup Hawaiian Holiday chopped
    macadamia nuts
1/2 stick melted butter
1/2 pint heavy cream
chocolate curls
1/2 cup Hawaiian Holiday
    whole macadamia nuts

Using a rolling pin, crush enough chocolate cookies to make 1-1/2 cups crumbs. Empty into a bowl and add ground nuts and cinnamon. Blend 1/2 cup melted butter with crumbs and nuts and pour into the center of a well-buttered 9 inch springform pan. Flatten mixture over bottom and press up along sides. Chill shell in refrigerator. In a medium bowl, beat sugar and eggs until mixture is light and stir in softened cream cheese.

Melt chocolate and dissolve coffee in one teaspoon of water, and add both to the bowl along with cocoa and vanilla, mixing thoroughly. Next, beat in sour cream and chopped nuts. Fold in remaining butter and pour batter into chilled shell. Bake at 350° for 45 minutes. Do not be alarmed if the cake seems quite liquid. It will achieve a firm and delicious consistency when chilled. When almost ready to serve, decorate cake with whipped cream, chocolate curls and whole nuts.

Anita De Domenico – Honokaa, Hawaii
Hawaiian Holiday Macadamia Nut Co.

texas praline cheesecake

1 cup graham cracker crumbs
3 tablespoons sugar
3 tablespoons margarine (melted)
3 8-ounce packages Philadelphia
    Brand cream cheese
1-1/4 cups packed dark brown sugar
2 tablespoons flour
3 eggs
1-1/2 teaspoons vanilla
1/2 cup finely chopped pecans

Combine crumbs, sugar, and margarine; press onto bottom of a 9 inch springform pan. Bake at 350° for 10 minutes.

Combine softened cream cheese, sugar and flour, mixing at medium speed on electric mixer until well blended. Add eggs, one at a time, mixing well after each addition. Blend in vanilla, stir in nuts. Pour mixture over crust. Bake at 450° for 10 minutes. Reduce oven temperature to 250° and continue baking for 30 minutes. Loosen cake from rim of pan, cool before removing rim of pan. Chill. Brush with maple syrup and garnish with pecan halves, if desired.

Sugar and Spice

italian cheesecake

3 pounds ricotta cheese
2 cups sugar
8 egg yolks, 8 egg whites
1/2 cup sifted all-purpose flour
2 teaspoons lemon rind, grated
1 teaspoon vanilla
1/2 cup heavy cream, whipped
graham cracker crumbs

Preheat oven to 425°. Beat ricotta until smooth. Gradually add 1-1/2 cups sugar and egg yolks, beating after each addition. Beat in flour, some lemon rind and vanilla. Beat egg whites with remaining sugar until stiff. Combine with whipped cream and fold into the ricotta mixture. Turn into a 12-inch springform pan which has been well buttered and sprinkled with graham cracker crumbs. Bake for 10 minutes, lower oven temperature to 350° and bake 1 hour. Turn off heat and allow to cool in oven with door open.

Angela G. Mancinelli – Honolulu, Hawaii

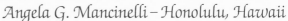

jerry's baked cheesecake

crust

2 packages graham crackers
    (cinnamon) crumbled fine
a handful of pecans
1/2 cup butter, melted
2 tablespoons sesame seeds
2 tablespoons oil
1 tablespoon vanilla
1/4 cup honey

filling

2 8-ounce packages cream cheese
2 eggs
1/2 cup honey
1/2 teaspoon lemon juice
2 teaspoons vanilla
2 tablespoons carob powder (opt.)
    or chocolate

topping

1 cup sour cream at room temperature
3 tablespoons honey
1 tablespoon vanilla
carob or chocolate powder (opt.)

To make the crust, chop nuts finely and combine with cracker crumbs and melted butter. Add sesame seeds, oil, vanilla and honey and blend thoroughly. Press into a 9-inch pie pan. Don't make crust too thick. It's rich, so make it fairly thin. Set aside.

For the filling, leave cream cheese and eggs out at room temperature until they assume room temperature. Mash cream cheese until smooth. Beat eggs with mixer in a bowl until frothy. Add to cream cheese in a bowl. Add honey, lemon juice and vanilla. Beat until smooth. Pour into prepared crust. Bake at 350° for 20 minutes.

For topping, mix sour cream, honey, and vanilla and put on top of cheesecake and bake an additional 5 minutes. Don't overcook.

....Be prepared for compliments!

Jerry Goldman – Los Angeles, California

caramel-pecan layered cheesecake

1 cup graham cracker crumbs
2 tablespoons granulated sugar
1/4 cup margarine
3 8-ounce packages Philadephia
    Brand cream cheese
3/4 cup granulated sugar
2 tablespoons flour
1 teaspoon vanilla
3 eggs
1/2 cup Kraft caramel topping
1/2 cup chopped pecans
1 tablespoon packed brown sugar
1-1/2 teaspoons margarine
1-1/2 teaspoons water
1/2 cup pecan halves
2 tablespoons Kraft caramel topping

Combine crumbs, granulated sugar, and margarine. Press onto bottom of a 9-inch springform pan. Bake at 325° for 10 minutes.

Combine softened cream cheese, granulated sugar, flour and vanilla, mixing at medium speed on an electric mixer until well blended. Add eggs, one at a time, mixing well after each addition. Reserve 1 cup cream cheese batter. Stir in 1/2 cup caramel topping. Spoon half of plain batter over crust, cover with caramel batter. Sprinkle chopped nuts over caramel layer. Spread remaining plain batter over crust and other fillings. Bake at 450° for 7 minutes. Reduce oven temperature to 250°, continue baking for 30 minutes. Loosen cake from rim of pan, cool before removing rim of pan. Chill.

In a saucepan, melt brown sugar and margarine. Add water. Bring to a boil, add nuts, cook 2 minutes, stirring constantly. Spread on wax paper to cool. Before serving, brush top of cheesecake with topping, garnish with nuts.

Sugar and Spice

pudding cake

crust

1 cup flour
1/2 cup chopped pecans or walnuts
1/2 cup margarine

filling

1 cup Cool Whip
1 cup confectioners' sugar
8 ounce package cream cheese
2 packages instant lemon pudding
3 cups cold milk
Cool whip, nuts – for frosting

Prepare crust by combining flour, nuts and margarine, and mixing well. Press into a 9 x 13-inch pan and bake at 375° for 15 minutes. Let it cool.

Beat together Cool Whip, confectioners' sugar and cream cheese until fluffy and spread on crust.

Mix pudding with milk until thick and spread on as second layer. Frost with additional Cool Whip and sprinkle chopped nuts on top. Let stand overnight in refrigerator.

Bill Gleason – Honolulu, Hawaii

german chocolate cheesecake

crust

1 cup flour
1/4 cup sugar
1 teaspoon grated lemon rind
1/2 teaspoon vanilla
1 egg yolk
1/4 cup soft butter

filling

1-1/2 6-ounce packages Baker's
    German sweet chocolate
3 eggs
1 cup sugar
3 8-ounce packages cream cheese
1/2 teaspoon vanilla
1 cup sour cream

For the crust, place all ingredients in a food processor. Blend until well mixed. Press over the bottom of a 9-inch springform pan. Bake 10 minutes at 400°. Cool. For the filling, melt chocolate. Cool. Beat eggs with sugar at a high speed in mixer until light and fluffy. Beat in cream cheese until well blended. Add cooled chocolate, vanilla, and sour cream and blend thoroughly.

Pour filling over crust and bake at 350° for 1 hour. Cool in pan and refrigerate.

….For a variation, top pie filling with 1/2 cup chopped pecans before baking.

Dorothy Souligny – Ponca City, Oklahoma

apple, apricot and almond tart

pastry—almond pâte brisée

1-1/2 cups all-purpose flour, unsifted
1 cup almonds
pinch of salt
1 tablespoon sugar
1/2 cup butter
4 tablespoons ice water

filling

6 to 8 medium (tart) apples
1 small jar apricot jam
1 lemon
2 tablespoons flour
1 tablespoon water

For the pastry, first, grind the almonds leaving skin on. Then add flour, salt, sugar and butter. Add ice water until consistency forms a ball. Refrigerate. Cut 1/4 of the pastry and save for the lattice on the top of the tart. Roll out the pastry on a floured board and place in a 10 inch tart pan. Place foil over the pastry. Fill with beans or rice and bake at 425° for 10 to 12 minutes. Carefully remove beans or rice and cool.

....Pâte brisée may also be made in a food processor.

For the filling, grate the rind and squeeze the juice of the lemon into a bowl. Peel, core, and thinly slice the apples into the bowl. Sprinkle with flour and toss to coat apples with flour and lemon juice. Arrange apple slices over tart in pan. Dissolve the apricot jam with 1 tablespoon water. Pour or brush 3/4 of jam over apple slices. Roll out the pastry you had set aside into a rectangular shape and cut lengthwise into 1/2 inch slices. Place these slices approximately 1-1/2 inches apart to form a lattice effect.

Glaze with remaining apricot jam and bake at 375° for 30 to 40 minutes or until golden brown.

....This tart may be served hot or cold and you may dust it with powdered sugar.

Valerie Arelt – Mill Valley, California

nutmeg

nutmeg

East Indies origin...essentially a seed, covered by a lacy, red fiber, it resembles a peach or apricot...a fashionable spice, European ladies and gentlemen carried tiny graters of unique design along with them to scrape the seed to flavor wine or food served in clubs, pubs or eating places they frequented.

Cookies

maggie's molasses cookies

6 to 7 cups flour
1 teaspoon salt
3 eggs
1 cup lard
1 pint of sorghum (molasses)
2 level teaspoons soda in a little water
dash of allspice

Sift flour, and put in a large bowl or in roaster pan. Make a well in the middle of the flour. Add the remaining ingredients into the well and mix with the flour. Place cookie mixture into the refrigerator to cool for a while.

Roll batter out and cut with your favorite cookie cutter. Grease and flour the cookie sheet. Bake at 350° for 10-12 minutes.

Sprinkle sugar on the freshly baked cookies or frost with a mixture of:
    1/2 teaspoon cloves
    1 teaspoon allspice
    1 teaspoon cinnamon
    1 teaspoon ginger

…you may substitute 1 cup sugar for the molasses and make a sugar cookie.

Maggie was Sally's great grandmother. This heirloom recipe dates back to pre-Civil War days.

Margaret Isabel Hughes Mires – Houston, Missouri

swedish gems

1 cup butter
1/2 cup sugar
2 cups flour
2 egg yolks
2 egg whites
1-1/2 to 2 cups nuts, chopped fine
    (preferably pecans)
raspberry jam

Cream butter and sugar. Add flour and egg yolks and beat 1 minute. Chill if you have time. Make balls of dough the size of small walnuts. Dip balls into slightly beaten egg whites then roll in chopped nuts. Place about 1-1/2 inches apart on a greased cookie sheet. They will spread a little. Preheat oven to 325° With a fingertip, make a slight indentation in center of each cookie. Fill with jam and bake about 12 minutes.

Michael Beebe – Honolulu, Hawaii

kourabiethes

1 pound clarified butter
1/2 cup confectioners' sugar
2 egg yolks
1 teaspoon baking powder
4 to 5 cups cake flour
1 cup almonds, ground and then toasted
2 ounces bourbon
whole cloves

Clarify butter, then refrigerate until firm but still soft enough to beat in electric mixer. Add sugar to butter and beat until puffy and lightly colored. Add egg yolks and continue beating until well mixed.

Sift flour and baking powder and add to butter, mixing in by hand. Use only enough of the flour to make a dough that is only firm enough to be shaped. Add the prepared almonds and bourbon. Shape into crescents and place on a cookie sheet. Press a whole clove into the center of each crescent.

Bake at 350° for 20 minutes. When done, sprinkle a very generous amount of sifted powdered sugar over the cookies. Store them with extra sugar.

Cleo Evans – Honolulu, Hawaii

world's best cookies

2 eggs
2 cups sugar
1 cup butter
1 cup ground raisins
2 cups oatmeal
2 cups flour
1 teaspoon soda
1 teaspoon salt
1 tablespoon vanilla

Sift flour, soda and salt together. Set aside. Cream butter and sugar. Then beat eggs and vanilla and add to butter mixture. Blend in flour mixture and raisins. Add oatmeal last and mix well. Drop by teaspoons on cookie sheets. Bake at 350° until lightly browned.

Gretchen Printup – Honolulu, Hawaii

snickerdoodles

1/2 cup butter
1/2 cup margarine
1-1/2 cups sugar
2 eggs
2-3/4 cups flour
2 teaspoons cream of tartar
1 teaspoon soda
1/4 teaspoon salt
2 tablespoons sugar
2 tablespoons cinnamon

Soften butter and margarine and mix together. Beat in the sugar and then the eggs. Sift flour, soda, cream of tartar and salt together and blend into mixture. Shape dough by rounded spoonfuls into balls. Combine sugar and cinnamon together and roll the balls in the mixture. Place 2 inches apart on an ungreased cookie sheet. Bake at 400° for 8-10 minutes.

Maxine Thomas – Honolulu, Hawaii

oatmeal butter cookies

1 cup powdered sugar
1/2 teaspoon baking soda
2 teaspoons vanilla
1-1/2 cups flour
1 cup oatmeal
1/2 pound butter

Mix all ingredients well, then roll into small balls. Flatten with fingers. Bake for 15 minutes at 350.° Yield about 50 cookies.

…I use instant oatmeal.

Evelyn Nordquist – Honolulu, Hawaii

chocolate chip cookies

1 cup vegetable oil
1 cup sugar
3/4 cup brown sugar (packed)
2 eggs
2 teaspoons vanilla
3 cups sifted flour
1 teaspoon salt
1 teaspoon baking soda
1 12-ounce package chocolate chips

In a bowl, mix oil, sugar, brown sugar, eggs and vanilla. Combine flour, salt, soda and chocolate chips and mix with sugar mixture. Drop by spoonfuls on an ungreased baking sheet. Bake at 375° for 8 to 10 minutes…the key is more flour than most recipes call for.

Jason Oliver – Honolulu, Hawaii

the everything cookie

1 cup shortening
1 cup brown sugar
1 cup white sugar
2 eggs
1 teaspoon vanilla
1 teaspoon soda
1 teaspoon salt
1-1/2 cups flour
3 cups rolled oats
    (dry oatmeal)
1/2 cup chopped dried apricots
1/2 cup raisins
1/2 cup chopped dates
1 cup mini chocolate chips
1/2 to 1 cup coconut, shredded or flaked
1 mashed banana (if large, you may
    need to add more flour)

Cream sugars and shortening together. Add vanilla and eggs. Mix. Blend flour, salt and soda. Add alternately with oats to sugar mixture. Stir in apricots, raisins, dates, chocolate chips, coconut, banana and extra flour if necessary.

Drop by spoonfuls on ungreased cookie sheet. Bake at 350° for 10 minutes or until lightly browned. Allow to cool 1/2 to 1 minute on cookie sheet before sliding off.

…these are good for someone who hates breakfast.

…also served with ice cream…just like a bowl of oatmeal with milk, only much more pleasant.

Shirley Lyon – Honolulu, Hawaii

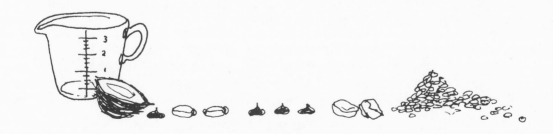

lace cookies

2-1/4 cups oatmeal
2-1/4 cups light brown sugar (1 pound)
3 tablespoons flour
1 teaspoon salt
1 cup butter
1 egg
1 teaspoon vanilla

Preheat oven to 375°. Have butter browned and egg slightly beaten. Combine dry ingredients and stir in butter. Add egg and vanilla and blend well. Arrange by 1/2 teaspoon at least 2 inches apart (about 6 on a cookie sheet). Bake at 375° for about 5 minutes or until lightly browned. Let cool and remove from cookie sheet.

Nancy Kreuger – San Antonio, Texas

macadamia shortbread hawaiian cookies

1 cup butter, softened
1/4 cup sugar
1 teaspoon vanilla
2 cups all-purpose flour
1/4 teaspoon salt
2 cups coconut flakes
1 cup powdered sugar
1/2 cup Hawaiian Holiday chopped macadamia nuts
1/4 cup Hawaiian Holiday finely ground macadamia nuts

Sift flour, measure and sift again with salt. Set aside. In a large bowl, cream butter, then add granulated sugar and cream until thoroughly blended. Add vanilla. Gradually beat sifted flour into creamed mixture until smooth. Mix in coconut and nuts. Shape into a roll, 1-1/2 inches in diameter and wrap in clear plastic wrap. Refrigerate at least 6 hours or overnight.

Slice roll at 1/4-inch intervals and place rounds on greased baking sheet. Bake at 300° for 20 minutes. Sift confectioners' sugar onto wax paper, reserving about 1/3 cup, and transfer baked cookies to it. Sprinkle tops lightly with remaining sugar. Let cool completely before storing in cookie tins. Makes about 3-1/2 dozen.

Anita L. DeDomenico – Honokaa, Hawaii
Hawaiian Holiday Macadamia Nut Co.

almond snowcap cookies

3/4 cup shortening
    (half butter or margarine)
3/4 cup confectioners' sugar
1-1/2 cups flour
3/4 cup raspberry jam

3 egg whites
3/4 cup sugar
1/2 cup flaked coconut
1 cup sliced almonds

Preheat oven to 350°. Cream shortening and confectioners' sugar. Blend in flour and press evenly in the bottom of a 13 x 9 x 2-inch ungreased pan. Bake for 12-15 minutes.

Spread jam over hot crust layer. Beat egg whites until foamy. Beat in sugar, 1 tablespoon at a time. Continue beating until stiff and glossy. Do not underbeat. Fold in coconut and 1/2 cup of the almonds. Place mixture over jam. Sprinkle remaining almonds over top. Bake for 20 minutes. Cool. Cut into squares about 1-1/2 inches each. Store in an airtight container. Makes about 4-1/2 dozen cookies.

Mabel Chapson – Honolulu, Hawaii

ice box cookies

1 cup brown sugar
1 cup white sugar
1 teaspoon vanilla
1 cup shortening
3 eggs
1 teaspoon soda
1 teaspoon baking powder
1 teaspoon salt
1 teaspoon cinnamon
3-1/2 cups flour
1 cup nuts

Mix sugar, vanilla and shortening well. Beat in the eggs. Sift soda, baking powder, salt and cinnamon together. Mix seasonings into sugar mixture. Add flour and blend well. Stir in nuts. With a little flour, roll dough into rolls and place in refrigerator. Makes 6 rolls. Slice rolls and bake at 350° for 10 minutes.

…I prefer pecans for nuts.

Florence Wallace – Ponca City, Oklahoma

ciasteczka z serem

(cream cheese cookies)

1 8-ounce package Philadelphia cream
    cheese
1/2 pound unsalted butter
2 cups unbleached flour
1-1/2 cups pureed prunes and apricots

To make the fruit puree, combine enough ready-to-eat pitted prunes and dried apricots in a blender to make 1-1/2 cups, adding just enough water to moisten to a soft consistency. Set aside.

Combine the cream cheese (softened to room temp.) with the butter and flour. Knead the dough. Roll out on a floured board 1/8 inch thick. Cut into 2-1/2 inch squares. Place 1/3 teaspoon fruit puree on each square. Fold the corners over and pinch to seal.

Place on a buttered and floured cookie sheet and bake at 375° for about 20 minutes. When cool, stack up on a platter or in a basket, a few at a time, and sprinkle with powdered sugar through a sieve. They are best when fresh. Yields 5 dozen.

Pat Wozniak – Honolulu, Hawaii

hershey cookies

8 to 10 small plain Hershey bars
1/2 cup pecans
2 cups flour
1 cup brown sugar
1 cup butter
1 egg yolk
1 teaspoon vanilla

Break up candy into small pieces. Chop pecans and set both aside. Sift flour, measure and set aside. Blend sugar and butter. Beat egg yolk lightly and add to sugar mixture. Add vanilla and mix in flour and blend well.

Shape small cookies and press onto a 10 x 15-inch cookie sheet and bake at 325° for 30 minutes. Sprinkle hot cookies with Hershey bar pieces. Spread the chocolate and sprinkle pecans on top. Cool and cut into 1/2-inch squares.

...these cookies keep very well in the refrigerator.

Jacque Monsour – Ponca City, Oklahoma

almond squares

crust

1 egg yolk
1/4 cup sugar
1 stick unsalted butter
1-1/4 cup flour

filling

1-1/2 sticks sweet butter
3 eggs
3/4 cup sugar
8 ounces almond paste

To make the crust, melt butter and mix together with egg yolk, sugar and flour. Mix with a fork. Press dough into an ungreased 9-inch square or round pie plate. Set aside.

For the filling, cut all the butter into cubes (1/4 inch) and place in a mixing bowl. Cut the almond paste into the bowl. Add sugar and eggs. Mix at medium speed until there are no lumps. Pour mixture into the prepared crust. Bake at 350° for 35-40 minutes. Allow to cool and slice into squares.

Pat Hookstratten Crowley – Beverly Hills, California

peanut butter balls

1-1/2 cups creamy peanut butter
2 sticks butter
1 box plus one cup powdered sugar

topping

7.5 ounce Hershey's chocolate bar
1/2 cake paraffin

Cream peanut butter, butter and sugar together in a large bowl. Mixture will be very stiff.

For topping, heat chocolate and paraffin in a double boiler. Roll dough into balls and dip into chocolate mixture by using the tines of a fork to keep too much chocolate from coating. Place on wax paper to cool and firm.

Judy Richardson – Kailua, Hawaii

brandy walnut balls

1/2 cup butter
1/2 cup sifted powdered sugar
1/8 teaspoon salt
1 tablespoon brandy
1/2 teaspoon vanilla
1 cup sifted flour
1/2 cup black walnuts, finely chopped

In mixer bowl, cream together butter, sugar and salt until fluffy. Stir in brandy and vanilla. Stir in flour and nuts. Mix well and shape into 3/4-inch balls. Place on an ungreased cookie sheet and bake at 325° for 20 minutes or until lightly browned. Cool and roll in additional powdered sugar.

Linda O'Connor – Honolulu, Hawaii

coconut squares

crust

1 cup sifted flour
1 stick softened butter
2 tablespoons ice water

filling

1-1/2 cups brown sugar
2 eggs, separated
1 cup grated coconut
1 cup chopped walnuts
2 tablespoons sifted flour
1/2 teaspoon baking powder
1 teaspoon vanilla
pinch of salt

For crust, mix flour and butter and add ice water. Line the bottom and sides of an 8 x 8-inch pan.

To make the filling, mix sugar, coconut and nuts in a bowl. Add beaten egg yolks and vanilla. Fold in beaten egg whites. Then add flour, baking powder and salt. Bake at 350° for 30-35 minutes. When cool, cut into squares and place in cupcake paper liners.

Claire Johnson – Honolulu, Hawaii

pecan pie surprize bars

1 18-ounce package yellow cake mix
1/2 cup melted margarine
4 eggs
1/2 cup brown sugar
1-1/2 cups dark corn syrup
1 teaspoon vanilla
1 cup chopped pecans

Reserve 2/3 cup cake mix. In a bowl, combine the remaining cake mix, melted margarine, and 1 egg. Mix until crumbly. Press into a well greased 13 x 9-inch cake pan. Bake at 350° for 15-20 minutes until a light, golden brown. While baking, blend the 2/3 cup cake mix, brown sugar, dark corn syrup, vanilla and the remaining 3 eggs. Beat at medium speed for 1-2 minutes. Pour over crust. Sprinkle with chopped nuts. Return to oven and bake 30-35 minutes. Cool and cut.

Charlotte Whitehurst – Ponca City, Oklahoma

chinese chews

1-1/2 cups flour
1/2 teaspoon salt
1 teaspoon baking powder
1 stick margarine or butter
1 box brown sugar
3 eggs
1 teaspoon vanilla
1 cup chopped nuts
1/4 cup powdered sugar

Sift flour, salt and baking powder together and set aside. Cream butter and sugar. Beat in eggs and vanilla. Blend in dry ingredients and nuts. Bake in a square pan at 350° for 30-45 minutes. Sprinkle with powdered sugar and cut while warm.

Kip McCormack – Greenville, South Carolina

chocolate mint sticks

4 eggs
2 cups sugar
1/2 pound butter
2 squares bittersweet chocolate
    (unsweetened)
3/4 cup flour
2 cups slivered almonds
1 teaspoon peppermint flavoring

frosting

1/3 cup cream or evaporated milk
5 tablespoons butter
dash of salt
1 box powdered sugar
1-1/2 teaspoons peppermint flavoring
2 squares unsweetened chocolate

Beat eggs until blended. Then beat in sugar until well creamed. Melt together butter and 2 squares chocolate. Add this to the egg and sugar mixture. Add almonds, flour and peppermint flavoring. Mix well. Spread on a long cookie sheet. Bake at 350° for 25-30 minutes. Cool, then frost.

To make frosting, boil cream or evaporated milk with 3 tablespoons butter plus a dash of salt. Add powdered sugar and mix well. Add peppermint flavoring. You may now tint it pink or green, if you wish.

Spread frosting on cooked baked cookie that is still in sheet form. Allow to harden. Then melt chocolate with 2 tablespoons butter and spread over hardened frosting with pastry brush. Put in refrigerator to set chocolate. Cut into sticks 1 x 4 inches when ready to serve. Marvelous!

Roberta Lear-Kauffman – Honolulu, Hawaii

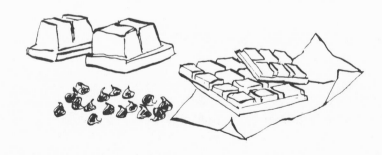

special brownies

1 stick (1/2 cup) butter
2 squares semi-sweet chocolate
1 cup sugar
2 eggs
1 teaspoon vanilla
1/2 cup flour
1/4 teaspoon salt
1 cup chopped walnuts

Melt the chocolate and butter in a saucepan over low heat. Remove from heat and let cool. In a separate bowl, mix the eggs and sugar. Add the chocolate mixture and vanilla, then the flour, salt and nuts. Pour into a well-greased 8 x 8-inch pan and bake at 350° for 30 minutes.

Jeanette Magoon – Honolulu, Hawaii

lemon bars
crust

1 cup butter
1/2 cup powdered sugar
1/2 teaspoon salt
2 cups flour

filling

4 eggs, beaten
2 cups sugar
1/2 teaspoon baking powder
1/4 cup flour
1/4 cup lemon juice
grated rind of 1 lemon

To make the crust, cream butter and sugar. Add salt and flour and mix well. Press into a 9 x 13-inch greased baking dish. Bake at 350° for 15-20 minutes.

For the filling, combine all ingredients and pour over the hot crust. Bake at 350° for 20-25 minutes. When done, sprinkle with powdered sugar. Cut into bars when cool.

Verna Lazarnick – Honolulu, Hawaii

chocolate "quickies"

1-1/2 cups sifted flour
1 teaspoon baking powder
1/2 teaspoon salt
2 eggs
1/3 cup salad oil
1 cup sugar
2 squares unsweetened chocolate,
    melted
1 teaspoon vanilla
1/2 cup nuts

Sift together dry ingredients. Beat eggs. Add oil, sugar, melted chocolate and vanilla and blend well. Add to flour mixture. Mix well. Drop by teaspoons onto oiled baking sheet. Decorate with nuts. Bake in a slow oven at 325° for 12 minutes. Makes about 3-1/2 dozen.

Jessie Brown – Honolulu, Hawaii

oatmeal crispies

1/2 cup soft butter or margarine
3 tablespoons brown sugar, packed
2 beaten eggs
1/2 cup whole wheat flour
1/2 cup rolled oats
1/4 teaspoon baking soda
1/2 teaspoon cinnamon
1 tablespoon milk
1/4 cup carob chips

Preheat oven to 350.° Grease a cookie sheet.

In a large bowl combine butter or margarine and sugar. Blend well. Add the beaten egg and milk and mix. Add the flour, oats, baking soda, carob chips and cinnamon and mix well. Drop by teaspoonfuls onto the cookie sheet, spacing the cookies about 1 inch apart. Bake for 15 minutes. Store leftovers in an airtight tin. Do not refrigerate. Yields about 3 dozen cookies.

Sugar and Spice

miniature pecan tarts

shells

1 3-ounce package cream cheese
1 stick butter
1 cup flour

filling

3/4 cup brown sugar
1 tablespoon butter
1 teaspoon vanilla
2 eggs
pinch of salt
2/3 cup pecans, chopped

For the shells, combine all ingredients, blending well. Refrigerate overnight. Shape into 24 small balls. Press into muffin tins.

For the filling, cream butter and combine with sugar, vanilla, salt and beaten eggs. Fill shells and sprinkle with nuts. Bake at 350° for 25 minutes. Remove from pan while hot.

Barbara Kott – Honolulu, Hawaii

caramel cuts

1/2 cup butter
2 cups brown sugar
2 eggs
1-1/2 cups flour
dash of vanilla
1 cup nuts (optional)

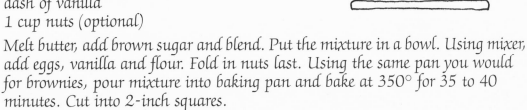

Melt butter, add brown sugar and blend. Put the mixture in a bowl. Using mixer, add eggs, vanilla and flour. Fold in nuts last. Using the same pan you would for brownies, pour mixture into baking pan and bake at 350° for 35 to 40 minutes. Cut into 2-inch squares.

...at Punahou, these have been a student favorite for years.

Tita Lyons – Honolulu, Hawaii
Food Director at Punahou School

miniature cheesecakes

crust

1 box zwiebach crackers
1 stick butter
1 tablespoon sugar (optional)

filling

4 eggs
1-1/4 cups sugar
3 8-ounce packages cream cheese
1 tablespoon vanilla
juice of 1 lemon
grated rind of 1 lemon

For the crust, soften the butter. Roll the crackers between folds of wax paper until crushed. Blend butter and crackers well and coat the inside of each well-greased muffin cup. "Small" sized muffin tins should be used.

For the filling, beat the eggs, sugar, cream cheese, vanilla, lemon juice and rind in a food processor. Mix thoroughly until smooth. Fill each tin 3/4 full with the cheese mixture and bake in a preheated oven at 350° for 20 minutes or until filling has risen and set firmly. Remove from pan immediately.

topping

1/2 cup sugar
1/2 pint sour cream
juice of 1/2 lemon

Blend sugar, sour cream and lemon juice well. Place in oven at 225° for 10-15 minutes. When muffins have cooled, spoon the topping on them and sprinkle with nuts or top with fresh fruit.

If fresh fruit isn't used, cheesecakes may be frozen.

Tita Kaspar – Aspen, Colorado

Cinnamon

cinnamon

unknown origin…essentially there are two types, the darker, pungent kind we know of, and a lighter, more delicate kind preferred in Mexico as a common addition to chocolate…in Arabia in days past, only the priests were permitted to gather it… even then, only after they placed the first bundle gathered on the altar of the sun god.

Breads & Muffins

whole wheat bread

2 packages dry yeast
1/2 cup warm water
1/2 cup brown sugar
2 tablespoons salt
2 tablespoons oil
2-1/4 cups warm water
6-7 cups whole wheat flour
    (4 cups wheat, 3 cups white)

Dissolve yeast in warm water and add a touch of the sugar (2 tablespoons). Mix salt, sugar, and 3 cups of flour (wheat first). Stir in oil, water and yeast. Add flour a cup at a time. Place in a large, greased bowl. Let rise 1 hour. Punch down, then place in two loaf pans and let rise 45 minutes. Bake at 375° for 40-45 minutes.

Gay Zuercher – Honolulu, Hawaii

oklahoma squaw bread

2 cups all purpose flour
1/2 teaspoon salt
4 teaspoons baking powder
1 cup milk

Mix dry ingredients, add milk and mix. Pat out on a flat surface (floured) until about 1/4 inch thick, as making biscuits. Cut dough in squares or circles about 4 inches each. Cut 1 or 2 slits in the center. Makes six single servings. Fry in deep, hot fat, fast. Fat should be deep enough in pan to cover dough. Serve hot with a barbecue dinner or serve with honey and jelly.

Kathryn Lessert – Ponca City, Oklahoma

applesauce loaf

1/2 cup margarine
1 cup sugar
2 eggs
1-3/4 cups sifted all-purpose flour
1 teaspoon salt
1 teaspoon baking powder
1/2 teaspoon baking soda
1/2 teaspoon cinnamon
1/2 teaspoon nutmeg
1 cup sweetened applesauce
1/2 cup chopped walnuts

glaze

1/2 cup confectioner's sugar
1 tablespoon water

Beat margarine and sugar till light. Add eggs, beat until light and fluffy. Sift together dry ingredients. Add to creamed mixture alternately with applesauce. Beat after each addition. Stir in nuts. Pour into a buttered and floured loaf tin, 9-1/2 x 5 x 8-inches. Bake at 350° for 1 hour. Cool in pan for 10 minutes. Remove to rack.

For glaze, mix confectioners' sugar and water together. Blend well. Brush over loaf while warm.

Barbara Bell – Aspen, Colorado

poppy seed loaf

1 thick loaf French bread
1 8-ounce package Swiss cheese, sliced
1/4 pound butter
1/2 cup green onion, chopped
3 tablespoons poppy seeds
3 teaspoons dry mustard

Mix all ingredients together except cheese. Cut crust off top, sides and end of bread. Slide knife through 3/4 of the way not through completely. Spread with butter mixture. Put 1/2 of a slice of cheese between bread slices. Coat with remaining mixture. Wrap in foil and bake at 400° for 20 minutes.

…Great with soups or salads.

Barbara Bell – Aspen, Colorado

french bread

1 package yeast
2 cups lukewarm water
4 cups sifted all-purpose flour
1 tablespoon sugar
2 teaspoons salt

Dissolve yeast in 1 cup lukewarm water. While yeast softens, sift flour, sugar, and salt together in a large bowl, then stir in the dissolved yeast. Add just enough of the second cup of water to hold the dough together. Mix until you have a soft, rather sticky dough. Cover with a clean cloth, set bowl in a warm spot (not near direct heat) and let rise until double in size…usually takes 2 to 4 hours.

When dough is high and spongy, punch down with fist and give good sound beating with hand. Divide in two parts and place each part in a greased, 6-inch round casserole. Cover again with cloth and let rise until almost double in size. Place in a 400° oven for 30 minutes until golden brown. Tap top and if it sounds hollow it is done. Let cool on rack.

Marylou Brogan – Honolulu, Hawaii

cheese almond bread

3-3/4 to 4 cups all-purpose flour
3/4 cup almonds, finely chopped
2 packages active dry yeast
1/4 cup butter or margarine
1/2 cup sugar
1/4 cup water
1/2 teaspoon salt
3/4 cup sour cream
2 eggs
1 teaspoon vanilla
1 slightly beaten egg white

cheese filling

1 8-ounce package cream cheese
1/4 cup sugar
1 egg yolk
1/2 teaspoon vanilla
1/2 cup almonds, chopped

In a large mixing bowl, combine 1-1/2 cups of the flour, the almonds and yeast. In a saucepan, heat butter or margarine, sugar, water, and salt until lukewarm (115-120°), stirring constantly until butter almost melts. Add to flour mixture, along with sour cream, eggs and vanilla. Beat at low speed for 1/2 minute, scraping sides of bowl constantly. Beat 3 minutes at high speed. Stir in as much of the remaining flour as you can mix with a spoon.

Turn out onto a lightly floured surface. Knead in enough remaining flour to make a moderately soft dough that is smooth and elastic (about 3 to 5 minutes). Shape into a ball, place in a greased bowl, turn once to grease surface. Cover, let rise till double (1-1/2 to 1-3/4 hours) punch down, divide in half. Cover, let rise 10 minutes.

cheese filling procedure:

In a small bowl, cream together all ingredients and stir in almonds.

On a lightly floured surface, roll half the dough to a 12 x 18-inch rectangle. Spread half of the cheese filling on dough to within 1/2 inch of edge. Roll up, starting from long side. Press ends of roll together, cut short slits about 1-1/2 inches apart in top of wreath shaped roll. Brush with some egg white. If desired, garnish with some sliced almonds and sprinkle with sugar.

Repeat process with remaining dough. Cover, Let rise till double (about 1 hour). Bake at 350° for 30 to 35 minutes. If necessary, cover with foil after 20 minutes of baking to prevent over-browning. Cool on a wire rack.

Bonnie Prior – Honolulu, Hawaii

cornbread

1 cup Bisquick
1 cup corn meal
1 egg
2 tablespoons oil
1 cup milk

Combine all ingredients in a bowl and beat until thoroughly blended.

Heat 5 tablespoons oil in a 10-inch iron skillet. Add batter to hot skillet. Bake at 425° about 20 minutes or until golden brown. This can also be used for corn muffins or corn sticks.

Lita Heller – Aspen, Colorado

onion cornbread

3/4 cup onion, chopped
1/4 cup butter
1 cup flour
1 cup yellow corn meal
3 teaspoons baking powder
1/2 teaspoon salt
2 eggs
1 cup milk
4 tablespoons mayonnaise
4 tablespoons grated Parmesan cheese

Saute 1/2 cup onion in butter about 5 minutes. Sift together flour, corn meal, baking powder and salt. Add beaten eggs and milk. Mix well then add sauteed onion. Spread batter in a greased 8-inch square or round pan. In a small bowl, blend mayonnaise, grated cheese and remaining 1/4 cup onion. Spread over top of batter. Bake at 350° for 30 minutes or until brown.

"Mike" Marshall – Priddis, Alberta, Canada

spoon cornbread

2 eggs, slightly beaten
1 8-1/2-ounce package corn
      muffin mix
1 8-ounce can creamed corn
1 8-ounce can whole kernel corn,
      drained
1 cup sour cream
1/2 cup butter, melted
1 cup (4 ounces) shredded Swiss cheese

Combine eggs, muffin mix, corns, sour cream, and butter. Bake in a pan 11 x 7 x 1-3/4 inches, at 350° for 35 minutes. Sprinkle shredded cheese on top. Bake until knife comes out clean.

Kent Vannoy – Lee's Summit, Missouri

mondel bread

3/4 cup vegetable shortening
3 eggs
1 cup nuts (walnuts or almonds)
      cut up
1 teaspoon cinnamon-sugar mixture
1 teaspoon salt
1 cup sugar
1 teaspoon vanilla
2-1/2 cups all-purpose flour
2 teaspoons baking powder
1 teaspoon lemon juice

Cream shortening, add sugar, eggs, 1/2 tsp. cinnamon-sugar mixture, and beat in mixer for almost 15 minutes. Add vanilla and lemon juice, then nuts. Add baking powder, salt and flour which have been mixed together. Use spatula and beat at lowest mixer speed for 1 minute. Sprinkle a little flour on cutting board. With spatula and knife roll 1/3 of the dough, then put into pan or greased cookie sheet. Flour hands and pat each portion of dough into shape of a long loaf, about 3 inches wide and 1 inch high. Repeat to make 3 loaves. Pat lightly on top and sprinkle with 1/2 tsp. cinnamon-sugar.

Bake at 350° for 30 to 35 minutes. Remove from oven, cut diagonally, and bake an additional 5 to 7 minutes at 400° to toast.

...may be used as a coffee cake, delicious!

George Johnston – Los Angeles, California

sesame herb toast or bread

1/4 pound butter
2 tablespoons sesame seeds
1/4 teaspoon marjoram
1 tablespoon chopped chives (optional)
1/4 teaspoon basil
1/4 teaspoon rosemary

Soften butter, mix with the rest of the ingredients and spread on bread. You can either put on slices and toast under broiler, or cut French bread diagonally and put on butter and wrap in foil and heat at 325° for 15 minutes.

Marjane Wall – Mill Valley, California

cheese bisquick

1-1/2 cups Bisquick
1/2 cup milk
1 egg
1-1/2 onion, finely chopped
1 tablespoon butter
1 cup sharp cheddar cheese, grated
2 tablespoons melted butter

Brown onion in 1 tablespoon butter. Mix Bisquick, milk, egg and browned onion and 1/2 of the grated cheese. Place in an 8 x 8-inch greased pan and dribble melted butter over top. Sprinkle with remaining cheese and bake at 350° for 25-30 minutes.

Jane Armstrong – Dallas, Texas

ada's rolls

3/4 cup butter, melted
1-1/2 cups sugar
1/2 cup nuts
5 teaspoons cinnamon
frozen bread loaves (unbaked dough)

Allow bread to thaw and cut into balls the size of walnuts. Roll balls in butter, then in sugar mixed with nuts and cinnamon. Place in ungreased angel food cake pan. Let rise and bake at 350° for 45 minutes.

Sugar and Spice

easy refrigerator rolls

2 cups lukewarm water
1/2 cup sugar
1-1/2 teaspoons salt
1/4 cup soft shortening
2 packages dry yeast
1 egg
6 to 7 cups sifted flour

Mix together water, sugar, salt and shortening. Add yeast and stir until dissolved. Stir in egg and beat in 3 cups flour until smooth. Work in remaining flour with hands using amount necessary to make dough easy to handle. Pound the dough, kneading is unnecessary. Place in greased bowl. Rub surface with soft shortening. Cover tightly with double thickness wax paper, then with damp cloth. Place in refrigerator until ready to use. Dampen cloth occasionally when in refrigerator. When dough rises, punch it down. When fresh rolls are desired, remove dough from refrigerator. Cut off amount needed and return remainder to refrigerator. Shape into rolls as desired and place in greased pan. Cover, let rise about 1-1/2 hours. Bake at 400° for 12-15 minutes. Makes about 3-1/2 dozen rolls.

Sugar and Spice

southern sour cream muffins

2 cups self-rising flour
2 sticks butter or margarine
1 cup sour cream

Melt butter and mix into flour. Add sour cream and mix. Bake in small muffin tins at 350° for 15-20 minutes. Makes approximately 4 dozen. Super for luncheon or brunch.

....Melt in your mouth.

Kip McCormack – Greenville, South Carolina

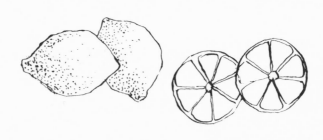

banana nut bread

1-3/4 cup sifted flour
1-1/4 teaspoon baking powder
1/2 teaspoon soda
3/4 teaspoon salt
2/3 cup sugar
1/3 cup oleo margarine
2 eggs
1/4 cup chopped nuts
1-1/4 cup banana pulp

Sift together flour, baking powder, soda, and salt. Gradually add sugar to oleo and cream until fluffy. Blend in one egg at a time to sugar mixture, mixing until smooth and light after each addition. Add nuts; add flour mixture, alternately with the banana pulp, blending well. Pour into a well-greased 9 x 5 x 3-inch loaf pan, pushing butter into corners. Bake in a 350° oven for 55 minutes or until browned. Cool on wire rack. For easier slicing, wrap in waxed paper when cool and store overnight.

Doris Mires, Ponca City, Oklahoma

orange date muffins

1 whole orange
1/2 cup orange juice
1 egg
1/2 cup chopped pitted dates
1/2 cup butter
1-1/2 cups flour
1 teaspoon baking soda
1 teaspoon baking powder
3/4 cup sugar
1 teaspoon salt

Cut orange into sections and blend until finely ground. Add juice, egg, dates and butter and blend. Mix dry ingredients in a separate bowl. Pour orange mixture over dry ingredients and stir lightly. Drop into 18 muffin paper cups and bake at 400° for 15 minutes.

Eva Pocklington – Edmonton, Alberta Canada

poi muffins

1-1/3 cups flour
1/2 teaspoon salt
1 tablespoon sugar
4 teaspoons baking powder
1 egg
2/3 cup poi
3 tablespoons butter
1/2 cup milk

Sift together dry ingredients, set aside. Beat egg and blend with poi, butter (melted but cooled) and milk. Combine with dry ingredients and spoon into oiled miniature (2-inch) muffin tins, 2/3 full. Bake at 400° for 25 to 30 minutes. Makes 18 muffins.

Michael Eith – Honolulu, Hawaii

bran muffins

1 cup hot water
2 cups Kellogg's All Bran Buds
1 cup Nabisco 100% Bran Cereal
1/2 cup margarine or butter
1-1/2 cups sugar
2 eggs
2-1/2 cups flour
2-1/2 teaspoons soda
1/2 teaspoon salt
2 cups buttermilk

Pour hot water over bran buds and allow to cool. Cream together margarine and sugar and add eggs. Sift together flour, soda and salt. Add to margarine and sugar mixture alternately with buttermilk. Add the cooled bran mixture, then add the Nabisco bran cereal. Mix well.

Store in tightly covered bowl (Tupperware is great) for as long as 6 weeks in refrigerator.

Spray muffins tins with "Pam" and then, half fill muffin tins…you can make as few as 2 at a time, or any amount. Bake at 375° for 20 minutes.

For variations…substitute whole wheat flour for white flour…substitute brown sugar for white sugar…add 1 teaspoon cinnamon…add 1/2 cup chopped nuts or raisins.

Howard C. Donnelly – Honolulu, Hawaii

287

Children's Snacks

Here are some ideas for nutritious snacks you can make from foods you might have in your kitchen right now.

....Banana chunks dipped in orange juice. Shake in a bag with chopped peanuts, spear with toothpicks.

....Celery stuffed with cottage cheese or a cheese spread made of any grated natural cheese moistened with plain yogurt or peanut butter.

....Cherry tomatoes stuffed with cottage cheese, a cheese spread, egg salad or tuna salad.

....Juice cubes you can make by freezing fruit juice in an ice cube tray, then use cubes to chill other fruit drinks.

....Fruit kebabs made of bite-sized fruit chunks, strung on a toothpick or skewer, can be served with a dip made of plain yogurt sweetened with a little honey.

....Raw vegetable sticks or pieces served with a dip made of cottage cheese mixed with catsup.

...."good for you soda pop." Mix chilled apple juice with club soda. For variety, try unsweetened grape or cranberry juice.

....Slices of apple spread with peanut butter or cheese spread.

....Bread sticks which are sold in the supermarket, try the plain ones or the type with sesame seeds.

....Jello-cottage cheese pudding – try this easy to make recipe from Joanna Yim.

Add the required water to a package of Jello and then turn the recipe over to the kids who stir in a container of cottage cheese, small or large, plain or with pineapple. Then refrigerate until firm. Joanna says there is no need to wait for partial jelling before adding the cottage cheese.

Lynne Friedlander & Denby Fawcett
Parent's Hotline – Honolulu Advertiser

turmeric

turmeric

Indian or Chinese origin...the limited
availability of saffron allowed the equally
vibrant color of this herb to be acceptable
and useful to those Persian sun worshippers
who held the golden crocus sacred as the
representation of the sun...magical
properties were attributed to it and pieces
of the root were hung about the necks of
children to act as charms.

Sugar and Spice
Peppermill Press, Inc.
P.O. Box 1810
Ponca City, Oklahoma 74602

Send me_____ copies of your cookbook at $16.95 per copy.
This includes postage, handling and taxes where applicable.
(Payable in U.S. Funds only)

Enclosed is my check or money order in the amount of $_____ .

Name_____

Address_____

City_____ State_____ Zip_____

Make checks payable to **PEPPERMILL PRESS, INC.**

Please gift wrap ☐

FROM: Peppermill Press, Inc.
P.O. Box 1810
Ponca City, Oklahoma 74602

TO:
Name_____
Address_____
City_____
State_____ Zip_____

MAILING LABEL—PLEASE PRINT

Sugar and Spice
Peppermill Press, Inc.
P.O. Box 1810
Ponca City, Oklahoma 74602

Send me_____ copies of your cookbook at $16.95 per copy.
This includes postage, handling and taxes where applicable.
(Payable in U.S. Funds only)

Enclosed is my check or money order in the amount of $_____ .

Name_____

Address_____

City_____ State_____ Zip_____

Make checks payable to **PEPPERMILL PRESS, INC.**

Please gift wrap ☐

FROM: Peppermill Press, Inc.
P.O. Box 1810
Ponca City, Oklahoma 74602

TO:
Name_____
Address_____
City_____
State_____ Zip_____

MAILING LABEL—PLEASE PRINT

Sugar and Spice
Peppermill Press, Inc.
P.O. Box 1810
Ponca City, Oklahoma 74602

Send me_____ copies of your cookbook at $16.95 per copy.
This includes postage, handling and taxes where applicable.
(Payable in U.S. Funds only)

Enclosed is my check or money order in the amount of $_____ .

Name_____

Address_____

City_____ State_____ Zip_____

Make checks payable to **PEPPERMILL PRESS, INC.**

Please gift wrap ☐

FROM: Peppermill Press, Inc.
P.O. Box 1810
Ponca City, Oklahoma 74602

TO:
Name_____
Address_____
City_____
State_____ Zip_____

MAILING LABEL—PLEASE PRINT